DON GIOVANNI

Opera in Two Acts

Music by

W. A. Mozart

Libretto by
LORENZO DA PONTE

After the play by
TIRSO DE MOLINA

English Version by
W. H. AUDEN
and
CHESTER KALLMAN

Ed. 2424

G. SCHIRMER, *Inc.*

DISTRIBUTED BY
HAL•LEONARD CORPORATION
7777 W. BLUEMOUND RD. P.O. BOX 13819 MILWAUKEE, WI 53213

© MCMLXI, by G. Schirmer, Inc.
International Copyright Secured
Printed in U.S.A.

Note

All rights of any kind with respect to this English translation and any part thereof, including but not limited to stage, radio, television, performance, motion picture, mechanical, printing, and selling, are strictly reserved.

License to perform this work in this translation in whole or in part must be secured in writing from the Publishers. Terms will be quoted upon request.

G. SCHIRMER, INC.

CAST OF CHARACTERS

DON GIOVANNI, a young nobleman

DON OTTAVIO

LEPORELLO, servant of Don Giovanni

IL COMMENDATORE, Donna Anna's father

MASETTO, a peasant

DONNA ANNA, betrothed to Don Ottavio

DONNA ELVIRA, a lady of Burgos

ZERLINA, betrothed to Masetto

Peasants, Musicians, Dancers, Demons

The scene is laid in Sevilla in the middle of the 17th century

DON GIOVANNI

Probably no single dramatic idea has inspired so many poets and playwrights of different times and countries as the legend of Don Juan. The Faust story would seem to have won a greater number of adherents among composers; but it is Don Juan and his encounter with the Stone Guest that has exerted a wider appeal among the creators of poetry and drama. Ultimately, these two legends — of Faust and Don Juan — were to become fused as one in the Gothically Romantic poems of Nikolaus Lenau, but this was a state of mind peculiar to Central Europe in the last century and has not persisted elsewhere. With Pushkin, Byron and Shaw, subtler philosophical refinements were brought to the Don Juan story; and, in our time, Don Juan has passed from the realm of drama into Freudian symbolism. Psychiatric jargon — at least that which is current among laymen — speaks unremittingly of the "Don Juan" complex.

Just where did this broadly ranging subject originate? We are told that the idea first appeared in medieval morality plays; but there remains no documentation. The legend itself seems to have sprung up around Seville and, like the Faust story, was based upon the exploits of a personage who had actually lived. The tale of Don Juan concerns itself with a member of the noble Tenorio family, Don Juan, alleged to have been a fourteenth-century perpetrator of plots against the womanhood of Seville.

The first play involving this subject — and one of the most memorable — to reach the stage was by the Spanish dramatist, Gabriel Tellez (1584-1648), who wrote under the pseudonym of Tirso de Molina. It was called *El Burlador de Sevilla y Convivado de Piedra* (The Rake of Seville and the Stone Guest). Though a pioneer in the field, it is by no means an unfinished product, nor, in any sense, a sketch. The plot development is masterly, the characterization finely drawn, the dramatic interplay engrossing to the modern reader. Its point of fullest similarity with later treatments of the legend lies, of course, in the appearance — at its climax — of the Stone Guest, the statue of the slain Don Gonzalo de Ulloa, who has been killed in a duel with Don Juan while defending his daughter's honor. Don Juan brazenly invites the statue to sup with him. To his consternation, the statue not only accepts but bids Don Juan join him at table in a nearby chapel. The dishes at their supper contain scorpions and snakes, the wine is gall and verjuice, the table music is a penitential psalm. At length, the statue vanishes and Don Juan is consigned to Hell.

This is, in short, the *clou* of the drama. Wherein it differs from subsequent versions lies in the number and nature of the women pursued by Don Juan, and the locale of the action (the first part takes place in Naples, and further developments are shifted to Seville). Although the exact date of the play's first performance is not recorded, we do know that it appeared in Spain about 1615. Its first translation came soon afterward in Italy; and with astonishing speed for those times, it crossed the ocean in its original tongue and was presented at Lima in 1623.

A whole series of plays by French and Italian authors now followed, practically all of them bearing the title *Le Festin de Pierre* (The Feast of Stone) or the equivalent *Il Convitato di Pietra*. There is some uncertainty as to whether the amusing catalogue of Don Juan's conquests was introduced by an Italian dramatist named Cicognini or by a compatriot, Giliberti, whose treatment of the subject was translated into French and given at Lyons in 1658. In any event, the most famous theatrical treatment, prior to the Mozart-Da Ponte *Don Giovanni,* was *Le Festin de Pierre* of Molière, produced at Paris in 1660. This French adaptation of the Tirso play aroused great controversy when it was first given, owing to the religious and social questions explored by Molière's plot. Don Juan is here an atheist; his cavalier treatment of a pious beggar casts reflections on the noble class in general; and altogether the play aroused such opposition that it was withdrawn after a relatively small number of performances. It is significant that just as Da Ponte avoided all the vexing social implications of Beaumarchais' comedy, *Le Mariage de Figaro,* in turning it to the needs of a libretto for Mozart, so did he succeed in dodging every touchy issue which might have been engendered by memories of Molière's *Le Festin de Pierre*. An interesting sidelight is thrown upon the emotions aroused by this play when one reads, in dissertations by modern Spanish critics on the Tirso de Molina drama and the theatrical literature derived from it, that Molière's Don Juan, in his atheism and his lack of gallantry toward the poor, is un-Catholic and un-Spanish. Evidently rape and seduction are rated in the Hispanic critical book as less deadly sins.

Other versions of the legend, some of them surviving, some discarded in the jungle law of literary evolution, include Rosimond's *Le Festin de Pierre* (Paris, 1669), Thomas Shadwell's *The Libertine Destroyed* (London, 1676), and Goldoni's *Don Giovanni Tenorio* (Venice, 1736), a play notable as the first on this theme in which Don Juan denounces Isabella (later Elvira, in the Mozart version), who keeps following him and upsetting his romantic activities, as mad. With the advent of the eighteenth century, this legend moved temporarily from the literary into the operatic arena, and it was not until the 1800's that Don Juan once more attracted such celebrated writers as Byron, De Musset, Dumas père, Merimée (in whose *Les Ames du Purgatoire* Don Juan repents and becomes a monk!), Pushkin and Zorrilla. Rostand and Shaw were to add the final postscripts to the Don Juan literature for the spoken drama.

The cycle of operas dealing with this subject started with Le Tellier's *Le Festin de Pierre,* given at Paris in 1713. Similar works by Righini and Gazzaniga followed in Italy, the latter (1787) exerting a tremendous influence upon the libretto which Da Ponte shaped for Mozart. It is here that mention is first made of Don Juan's lawful wife (Elvira) as having come from the city of Burgos, an allusion carried over into Mozart's *Don Giovanni* itself; and, indeed, the script by Da Ponte parallels in many fundamental ways Gazzaniga's *Il Convitato di Pietra,* whose libretto was written by a rival poet named Bertati.

Gluck composed his famous ballet, *Don Juan,* on the same plot (with choreography by Gaspare Angiolini), a work notable not only for its own dramatic validity but also for the fact that its magnificent final number, in which Don Juan is torn to pieces by the demons of Hell, was carried over by the composer into his opera, *Orfeo ed Euridice,* first produced in the following year, as the Dance of the Furies. There have been latter-day adaptations of this same ballet score to new choreography by Michel Fokine (1936) and Leonide Massine (1958). Other noteworthy operas on the Don Juan subject, coming after the Mozart *Don Giovanni* are Dargomijski's *The Stone Guest* (1872) and Eugene Goosens' *Don Juan de Mañara* (1929), the dramatic source of which stems from a related legend of Seville.

In the course of these constant reworkings of the same subject, certain characters from the original Tirso play disappeared, others were developed, still more were retained under different names. The Isabella of the early plays gradually becomes Elvira; Catalinón, Don Juan's servant, evolves into Arlecchino, Sganarelle, and later Leporello. Aminta, Tisbea, Rosalba, rustic or fisher maidens with whom Don Juan has his fling, are finally rolled together into Da Ponte's Zerlina. Donna Anna is at first more or less of an incidental character, important to the development of the plot as Don Gonzalo's (later Don Pedro's) daughter, but not especially expressive on her own. It is only in the Mozart *Don Giovanni* that she becomes a commanding figure. Don Ottavio thrives as a forceful character in the Tirso and Molière plays, the fierce adversary of Don Juan; but he is emasculated by Mozart's librettist, Da Ponte, into an Italian tenor-bystander. Significantly, only three basic characters remain the same throughout all of the legend's various dramatic mutations: Don Juan, his servant and the statue. These are paramount.

How Mozart came to set this subject to music is a well known story, to be found in all the standard history books, and need not detain us here at length. His *Le Nozze di Figaro,* first given at Vienna in 1786, reaped a tremendous success in the same year at Prague; and full of gratitude, Mozart promised the premiere of his next opera to that city. Lorenzo Da Ponte, the ubiquitous librettist who was born in Italy, labored for years in Vienna, passed onward to London, and ended his career as a resident of New York and its environs, provided the book. The famous Casanova, then residing not far from Prague, is alleged to have written a few of the lines in the second act (supposedly the recitativo introducing Don Ottavio's *Il mio tesoro*), and to have given his expert advice on the atmosphere of the plot. Mozart composed the music swiftly, some of it in Vienna and the remainder in Prague, leaving the writing of the overture until the night before the first performance (some recent authorities claim it was the dress rehearsal). The premiere, on October 29, 1787, was an overwhelming success.

When the work was repeated several months later in Vienna, with a different cast of singers, Mozart added three numbers to the score, in order to please the performers at hand. The tenor, Francesco Morella, who sang Don Ottavio, found the aria *Il mio tesoro* too floridly difficult for his limited technique; and so this was replaced with the more sustained *Dalla sua pace.* Caterina Cavalieri, the Donna Elvira, demanded a grand *scena.* Thus the recitativo *In quali eccessi, o Numi,* followed by the aria *Mi tradì,* one of the greatest vocal inspirations ever to have come from Mozart's pen, was written for the Vienna performance. The soubrette, Luisa Mombelli, who sang Elvira, also demanded an additional number. As a result, Mozart inserted the comic duo, *Per queste tue manine,* for Zerlina and Leporello (now invariably omitted) in the second act.

Despite these accommodations on the part of the composer, *Don Giovanni* was not at first a success in Vienna, only gradually taking hold of the Austrian public. During the following century, its fame became international, traveling throughout Europe and reaching New York in 1826, when the celebrated company headed by Manuel Garcia and including gifted members of his family (notably his daughter Maria, later to be known as Maria Malibran) brought the work to America. It is now, at this time of writing, not only one of the most durable members of the repertoire but perhaps the sole opera which has no detractors. Polemics still rage, even at this late date, about the stage works of Gluck, Beethoven, Weber, Rossini, Puccini, Wagner and Strauss; but no voice is lifted against *Don Giovanni.* Musicians of every esthetic persuasion bend the knee to this extraordinary work. Labelled by Mozart in his thematic catalogue as an *opera buffa,* and in the libretto as a *dramma giocoso* (comedy-drama), it seems to have achieved a synthesis of the theater arts as has no other opera before or since. Working along conventional lines — the usual sequence of "set numbers" linked by *recitativo* both "dry" (accompanied by harpsichord alone) and "instrumented" (bolder in style, fused dramatically with the colors of the orchestra), Mozart has achieved an unbroken architectural line — except for a few places in the second act, where the libretto itself bogs down in an excess of detail — and a wealth of expressive spirit that stand beyond compare: utter freedom within the bounds of classical art.

Over the course of years, *Don Giovanni* has developed in performance a tradition of all-star casts not dissimilar to the custom which used to mark most presentations of Meyerbeer's *Les Huguenots.* Perhaps the most renowned agglomeration within present memory held the stage at the Metropolitan Opera House in 1929 with Rosa Ponselle as Donna Anna; Elisabeth Rethberg as Elvira; Editha Fleischer as Zerlina; Ezio Pinza as Don Giovanni; Beniamino Gigli as Don Ottavio; Pavel Ludikar as Leporello; and Leon Rothier as the Commendatore. More recent protagonists of the title rôle who have appeared internationally with distinction are John Brownlee, Cesare Siepi and George London.

NOTES ON PERFORMANCE

No more eloquent commentary on changing tastes in opera may be found than in the introductory notes by the late Henry Edward Krehbiel written in 1900 for the previous Schirmer edition of *Don Giovanni.* Mr. Krehbiel, a solid and respected reviewer of his time, expressed himself as follows about the opera's epilogue (closing sextet) which comes on the heels of Don Giovanni's damnation: "This finale was long ago discarded, and though Mozart set it to music, he did it in a manner which tells more plainly than the situation that it is an anti-climax, that the opera reached its end with the death of its hero". Indeed, Mr. Krehbiel's post-Wagnerian point of view has been shared by many opera producers in Central Europe; and this writer recalls hearing, as recently as 1937, a performance of *Don Giovanni* at the Vienna State Opera, with Pinza singing the title rôle, in which the finale was omitted. Such an approach today, of course, has universally disappeared; and the genius of Mozart in keeping his daemonic hero within the framework of the period by adding the superb final sextet, is now fully recognized. This epilogue is necessary for still another reason — dramatically — so that the audience might learn the fate of the characters other than Don Giovanni. Any performance without it would be unthinkable.

Occasionally a tenor who is singing Don Ottavio with an inadequate technique will take refuge in "tradition"; and because Francesco Morella omitted *Il mio tesoro* at the first Vienna performance in favor of the newly written and much easier *Dalla sua pace,* he will follow suit and do the same. This is, in reality, an evasion, for since the early 1800's every Ottavio worth his salt has sung both arias — so wonderfully contrasted — in the same performance: *Dalla sua pace* in Act One and *Il mio tesoro* in the courtyard scene of Act Two.

Trial and error, culminating in tradition, has decreed that the added duet, *Per queste tue manine,* wherein Zerlina drags Leporello by the hair and threatens him with a razor, should — through its utter superfluity — be suppressed. The point is just; but this omission, though simple on the surface, involves a grave problem. The unwanted duet modulates into Elvira's wonderful aria, *Mi tradi,* which closes this entire musical fragment added for the Vienna performance. An effective contrast may be secured, in theory, between the brash, chattering duet for the two *buffo* characters (Zerlina and Leporello) and the tremendously dramatic *Mi tradi.* When the duet is amputated from the score and Elvira's solo retained, contrast and theatrical impulse are lessened, the action is reduced to a string of arias. Thus, although printed in this score for use in the second act — as the culminating chunk of the added Vienna fragment — the aria is heard more effectively when placed in the second scene of Act One, just after Leporello has finished reading to Elvira, with jolting irony, the catalogue of Don Giovanni's sweethearts. What more natural than that the disillusioned woman, on Leporello's exit, should burst into the melody of indignation and sorrow poured out by Elvira in this incomparable aria? Thus was the number placed by Tullio Serafin when he directed the Metropolitan Opera revival of 1929, and the result was impressive. Sometimes the aria is omitted entirely in performance "for reasons of dramatic continuity". This means, in plain English, that the Donna Elvira of the evening is not equal to its vocal difficulties.

In earlier years, her rôle was considered the most important among the opera's three sopranos. An old playbill of the Metropolitan's opening season (1883) lists such noted singers as Emmy Fursch-Madi as Donna Anna, Marcella Sembrich as Zerlina, adding significantly: *"and* Christine Nilsson as Elvira". She is Don Giovanni's lawful wife, the female fulcrum of the plot, around whom Anna and Zerlina revolve as passing incidents. In all of the concerted numbers, moreover, her music is written at a lower pitch than that of Donna Anna, demanding greater amplitude and darker color — in other words, the attributes of a full dramatic soprano. And yet, because of Donna Anna's two great solo arias, it has become a tradition in recent times for the first dramatic soprano of the house to sing this part, while Elvira (with a few prominent exceptions) is turned over to secondary "utility" artists. As a consequence, Donna Anna's first aria, the imperious *Or sai, che l'onore* is generally sung with grand effect by a rafter-shaking voice; while the second aria, *Non mi dir*, with its high, rapid-fire *fioriture,* finds the Brünnhilde-Turandot-Donna Annas for a night generally falling on their faces. The singer of this part should, in all adequacy, be not a full dramatic soprano, but a *lirico spinto* (lyric-dramatic), as indicated by Mozart's vocal distribution in the ensembles.

We come, finally, to the music of Don Giovanni himself, which was written for a baritone, or high bass, of fairly restricted range. One advantage in casting a Don Giovanni of dark vocal quality would lie in the effect — so perceptively pointed out by the composer Charles Gounod in his discerning essay on the opera's hundredth anniversary (1887) — of three bass voices united in the tragic music which accompanies the death of Don Pedro after the duel, to the contrasting orchestral glint of woodwinds as the rising moon sheds its light upon the scene. Elsewhere in the part, a dark voice proves somewhat of a handicap by reason of the bright quality and high-lying *tessitura* demanded by much of the music, especially the second-act serenade. Above all, a contrast in color is needed between the burly bass sound of Leporello and the reedier, more aristocratic voice of Don Giovanni (Manuel Garcia, who won great fame in this part, was a tenor).

There are few, if any, cuts in *Don Giovanni,* save for the Zerlina-Leporello duet and an occasional line or two of "dry" recitativo. Other Mozart operas are treated less deferentially in modern performance; but with *Don Giovanni* scarcely a phrase is deleted . . . and whenever this does happen, it is the responsibility of the director in charge rather than the dictate of any fixed tradition.

Robert Lawrence

INDEX

ACT II

Don Giovanni

Overture

Lorenzo da Ponte
English version by
W. H. Auden and Chester Kallman

Wolfgang Amadeus Mozart

© MCMLXI, by G. Schirmer, Inc.
International Copyright Secured

Printed in U.S.A.

Moderato.
p
p
f
Wind
Vln
p
Fl.
Fag.
p
Vlns.
Vlns.
p
f
p
f
p
Wind
cresc.
Tutti
f

Tutti Vlns Tutti Vlns.

sf p sf p

Wind f Strs. f p p f p f p f p

f p p

f

Ob.
Fl.
Ob.
Fl.
Str.
Fl.
Str.
Wind.

Vln.

cresc.
Wind.
Str.

Tutti.
f
Vln.
p
Vln.
Fag.

Act I.

Nº 1. Introduction.

Scene — A Garden, Night.

Leporello, in a cloak, discovered watching before the house of Donna Anna; then Donna Anna and Don Giovanni, afterwards the Commandant.

L.
vo-glio più ser - vir, e non vo-glio più ser - vir, no, no, no,
more a ser-vant be, Would no more a ser-vant be, No, no, no,
p
(facing the palace)
no, no, no, non vo-glio più ser-vir.
no, no, no, I would a mas-ter_ be.
Oh che ca-ro galant-
What a dif-fer-ence be-
sf p
sf p
uo-mo!
tween us!
Voi star dentro col-la bel-la, ed io far la sen-ti
Warm you lie_in arms of beau-ty While I freeze on sen-try
sf p
sf p
nel-la, la sen-ti-nel-la, la sen-ti-nel-la!
du-ty, on sen-try du-ty, on sen-try du-ty;
Vo - glio
I would
fp
far il gen-til - uo-mo, e non vo-glio più ser -
like to play the mas-ter, Would no more your serv-ant
tr
f
fp
vir, e non vo-glio più ser-vir, No, no, no, no, no, no, non vo-glio
be, Would no more your serv-ant be, No, no, no, no, no, no, I would a

più ser-vir. Ma mi par, che ven-ga gen-te; ma mi par, che venga
mas - ter_ be. What was that? We're in for trou-ble. What was that? We're in for
L.
gen-te; non mi vo-glio far sen-tir, ah non mi vo-glio far sen-tir, non mi
trou-ble. This is not the life for me, no, This is not the life for me. This is
cresc.
f
p
L.
vo - glio far sen - tir, No, no, no, no, no, non mi vo - glio far sen-
not the life for me, No, no, no, no, no, This is not the life for_
L.
tir.
me.
Tutti.
(Hides himself.)
cresc.
f
Donna Anna. (Holding Don Giovanni firmly by the arm.)
A.
(her voice sti-fled by agita-tion.)
Non spe-rar, se non m'uc-ci - di, ch'io ti la-sci fug-gir mai.
No, you won't, you shan't es-cape me, I will nev-er_ let_ you_ go.
Strings.
Tutti.
fp
fp
fp
f
p
f

Donna Anna. (her
Don Giovanni. (Trying to conceal his features.)
Non spe-
No, you
Don-na fol-le! indar-no gri-di, chi son io, tu non sa-prai.
Do not scream! wake the household. Kiss me, dear, and let me go!
You'll
Leporello.
Che tu-
Mas-ter
Str.
fp
f
voice gaining strength)
rar, se non m'uc-ci-di, ch'io ti la-sci fug-gir mai, non spe-
won't, you shan't es-cape me! I shall nev-er let you go! No, you
Don-na fol-le! in-dar-no gri-di, chi son io tu non sa-
Do not scream! wake the house-hold. Kiss me, dear, and let me
You'll
mul-to! o ciel! che gri-di! Il pa-
curs-ing, the la-dy scream-ing, How am
p
(with full strength.)
rar, ch'io ti la-sci fug-gir mai. Gen-te! ser-vi-al tra-di-to-re!
won't, I will nev-er let you go! Fire and mur-der! Save me! Seize him!
(almost
prai, no, tu non sa-prai. Ta-ci, e
go! Now! Now let me go. Stop that
dron in nuo-vi guai.
I to get a-way?
fp
cresc.

(freeing herself)
A.
hissing; tries to cover her mouth)
Scel-le-ra-to!
Fire and mur-der!
Scel-le-ra-to!
Try to stop me!
G.
tre-ma al mio fu-ro-re!
noise or I shall hurt you.
Scon-si-glia-ta!
Stop, I tell you!
Scon-si-glia-ta!
Stop, I tell you!
L.
Sta a ve-
It's a
Str. & Cor.
f p cresc. fp p
(turning to the palace)
Gen-te! ser-vi!
Help me! Save me! (seizing her roughly)
Co-me fu-ria di-spe-ra-ta ti sa-
From my un-re-lent-ing fu-ry You shall
Ta-ci, e tre-ma!
Must I hurt you?
Que-sta fu-ria di-spe-
From her un-re-lent-ing
der che il li-ber-ti-no mi fa-rà pre-ci-pi-tar.
ver-y pret-ty pick-le, And I can-not get a-way
Che tu-
Mas-ter
Tutti
prò per-se-gui-tar.
nev-er get a-way.
Co-me fu-ria di-spe-ra-ta, di-spe-
From my un-re-lent-ing, my a-veng-ing
ra-ta mi vuol far pre-ci-pi-tar,
fu-ry I had bet-ter get a-way.
Que-sta fu-ria di-spe-
From her un-re-lent-ing
mul-to!
curs-ing,
oh ciel, che gri-di!
the la-dy scream-ing,

A.
G.
L.
ra - ta, ti sa - prò per -
fu - ry You shall nev - - - - er
ra - ta mi vuol far pre -
fu - ry I had bet - - - ter
Sta a veder che il li - ber - ti - no mi fa - rà pre - ci - pi - tar, sta a veder che il li - ber-
Well, we're in a pret - ty pick - le; How am I to get a - way? Well, we're in a pret - ty
se - - gui - tar. Scel - le - ra - to! Scel - le -
get a - way. Fire and mur - der! Try to
ci - - pi - tar. Scon - si - gliata! Scon - si -
get a - way. Stop, I tell you! Stop, I
ti - no mi fa - rà preci - pi - tar.
pick - le; How am I to get a - way?
ra - to! Gen - te! ser - vi! Co - me fu - ria di - spe -
stop me! Save me! Help me! From my un - re - lent - ing
glia - ta! Ta - ci, e tre - ma! Que - sta
tell you! I shall hurt you. From her
Sta a ve - der che il li - ber - ti - no mi fa - rà pre - ci - pi - tar.
It's a ver - y pret - ty pick - le, And I can - not get a - way.

A.
ra - ta, ti sa - prò per - se - gui - tar, co - me fu - ria di - spe -
fu - ry You shall nev - er get a - way. From my un - re - lent - ing,
G.
fu - ria di - spe - ra - ta mi vuol far pre - ci - pi - tar, que - sta
un - re - lent - ing fu - ry I had bet - ter get a - way. From her
L.
Che tu - mul - to, oh ciel, che gri - di!
Mas - ter curs - ing, the la - dy scream - ing,
ra - ta, di - spe - ra - ta, ti sa -
my a - veng - ing fu - ry You shall
fu - ria di - spe - ra - ta mi vuol
un - re - lent - ing fu - ry I had
Sta a veder che il li - ber - ti - no mi farà pre - ci - pi -
Well, we're in a pret - ty pick - le; How am I to get a -
Ob. Fag. & Str.
prò per - se - gui - tar.
nev - er get a - way.
far pre - ci - pi - tar.
bet - ter get a - way.
tar, sta a veder che il li - ber - ti - no mi farà pre - ci - pi - tar, sta a veder che il li - ber -
way? Well, we're in a pret - ty pick - le; How am I to get a - way? Well, we're in a pret - ty

A.
ti sa - prò per - se - gui -
You shall nev - - - - er get a -
G.
mi vuol far pre - ci - pi -
I had bet - - - ter get a -
L.
ti-no mi fa-rà pre-ci - pi-tar, sta a veder che il li - ber - ti-no mi fa-rà pre-ci - pi -
pick-le; How am I to get a-way? Well, we're in a pret-ty pick-le; How am I to get a -
(Seeing the Commandant approach, she runs into the house.)
tar.
way.
(Don Giovanni haughtily confronts the Commandant.)
tar.
way.
(The Commandant enters hastily, a torch in his left hand, a sword in his right.)
tar.
way?
Tutti.
ff
ff
The Commandant. (with agitation, but energetically)
C.
Lascia-la, in - de - gno, bat - ti - ti me - co!
Where is the vil-lain? Draw, sir, and fight me!
p
cresc.
Don Giovanni. (slightingly)
Va, non mi de - gno di pu - gnar te - co.
No! Pride for - bids me to draw on grey-beards.
Co - sì pre - ten - di
Faint-heart-ed cow - - ard!
f
p
f

G.
C.
L.
Va, non mi de - gno, no!
No! Pride for-bids me, No!
da me fug-gir?
I chal - lenge you.
Co-sì pre-ten-di da
Faint-heart-ed cow-ard! I
Leporello.
(Po-tessi al-me - no di quà par-tir!
If I could on - ly get out of here!
mezza voce
più voce
(draws)
Mi-se-ro! Mi-se-ro! Mi-
Force me not! Force me not! Do-
me fug-gir? Bat-ti-ti!
chal-lenge you. Draw, I say!
po-tessi al-me - no di quà par-tir!)
If I could on - ly get out of here!
(He strikes the torch out of the Commandant's hand.)
(First bout: the Commandant attacks.)
se - ro! at - ten-di se vuoi mo-rir!
tard, on guard, then! Your death is near.
(They fight.)
(2nd bout: Don G. attacks.)
(3rd bout.)
(The Commandant falls mortally wounded.)

(The moon rises slowly;
Andante.
Don Giovanni. sotto voce.
Ah! già ca - de il scia - gu -
Ah, he's fall - en! Ah, he's
The Commandant. (sinking slowly, leaning on his sword)
Ah! soc - cor - so! son tra - di - to! l'as - sas -
Ah, I'm wound-ed! Ah, I'm dy-ing! God, pro -
Leporello.
Qual mi - sfat - to!
Who has fall - en?
Andante.
Vls. Ob. & Cor.
pp
lights appear in the palace-windows: great excitement within: servants hasten with torches across the background behind the closed gate)
ra - to, af - fan - no - so e a - go - niz - zan - te già dal
dy - ing! Pay-ing dear - ly for his fol - ly. On this
si - no m'ha fe - ri - to, e dal
tect my child from e - vil! From this
Qual ec - ces - so! En - tro il sen dal - lo spa -
Who is dy - ing? How I shiv - er, how I
se - no pal - pi - tan - te veg - go l'a - ni - ma par -
world of love and beau - ty He must close his a - ged
se - no pal - pi - tan - te
mor - tal scene of sor - row
ven - to pal - pi - tar il cor mi sen - to!
shud - der! Root - ed to the spot by ter - ror,

(Servants return with Don Octavio, and hasten with him from the street into the palace)

G.
tir, veg - - go l'a - ni - ma par - tir, già dal
eye, Now must close his a - ged eye. On this

C.
sen - to l'a - ni - ma par - tir,
My im - - mor - tal soul must fly,

L.
Io non sò che far, che dir, io non sò che far, che dir, en - tro il sen dal - lo spa -
I can nei-ther move nor cry, I can nei-ther move nor cry. How I shiv - er, how I

G.
se - no pal - pi - tan - te veg - - go l'a - ni - ma par -
world of love and beau-ty Now must close his a - ged

C.
sen - - to l'a - - ni - - ma par - -
My im - mor - tal soul must

L.
ven - to pal - pi - tar il cor mi sen - to, io non sò che far, che dir, io non sò che far, che
shud - der! Root - ed to the spot by ter - ror, I can nei - ther move nor cry, I can nei - ther move nor

G.
tir.
eye.

(Dies.)

C.
tir.
fly.

L.
dir!
cry.

Ob. Vln.

p

Fl. Fag.

Recit. (Sotto voce, throughout this scene.)
Don Giovanni.
Le - po - rel - lo, o - ve se - i?
Are you there, Le - po - rel - lo?
Leporello.
Son
I
(Don G. sheathes his sword and dons his cloak)
quì per mia di - sgra - zia; e
on - ly wish I was - n't. Are
Don Giovanni.
vo - i? Son quì.
you there? Of course.
Leporello.
Chi è
Are
mor - to, voi, o il vec - chio?
you a ghost? Is he one?
Don Giovanni.
Che do - man - da da be - stia! il vec - chio.
What an im - bec - ile ques - tion! He's done for.
Leporello.
Bra - vo! due im - pre - se leg - gia - dre! Sfor - zar la fi - glia, ed am - maz - zar il
Bra - vo! Pret - ty good for one eve - ning. To rape the daugh - ter and then skew - er the
pa - dre!
fa - ther!
Don Giovanni.
L'ha vo - lu - to, suo dan - no!
He com - pelled me; I had to.
Leporello.
Ma donn' An - na, - cosa ha vo - lu - to?
And Donn' An - na... al - so com - pelled you?
Don Giovanni.
Ta - ci, non mi sec - car! Vien me - co,
Si - lence! No more from you. Re - mem - ber,
(Threatening to strike him.)
se non vuoi qual - che co - sa an - cor tu.
you can join the old man if you wish.
Leporello.
Non vo' nul - la, Si - gnor, non par - lo più.
From now on I'll be dumb as an - y fish.
(Exeunt.)

20
Donna Anna. (agitatedly descending the steps with D. Octavio, and servants bearing torches)
Don Octavio. (Raising his drawn sword.)
A.
O.
Ah! del padre in pe-ri-glio in soc-cor-so vo-liam! Tut-to il mio san-gue
Quick! His life is in dan-ger. We must come to his help. I will de-fend him.
O.
A.
Donna Anna.
ver-se-rò, se bi-so-gna: ma dov'è il scel-le-ra-to? In que-sto lo-co.
I will save him or per-ish. But I see and hear no one. I fear some e-vil.
Attacca.
Nº 2. "Ma qual mai s'offre, oh Dei."
Recit. and Duet.
Allegro assai.
Fl.
Ob.
Vln.
Viol. Fag. Cor.
(Seeing the corpse) Donna Anna.
A.
Ma qual mai s'of-fre, oh Dei, spet-
What, O God, do I see! What
A.
(sinks down beside the body)
ta-co-lo fu-ne-sto agli oc-chi mie-i!
spec-ta-cle of hor-ror ap-pears be-fore me!
A.
Il
It
44917

(throws herself upon the corpse)
D.Octavio.
D.Anna.
A.
O.
A.
Padre, padre mi-o! mio ca-ro padre! Si-gnore! Ah, l'assas-si-no mel tru-ci-
can't be! Not my fa-ther! Speak to me, fa-ther! Who did this? Ah, the as-sas-sin has struck him
(examining the corpse more carefully)
dò. Quel san-gue quel-la pia-ga
down! He's wound-ed! Look, he's bleed-ing!
Cl. Ob. Fag.
f
p
quel volto tin-to e co-per-to del co-lor di mor-te.
So si-lent, so still and so un-na-tu-ral-ly pal-lid!
(D. Octavio offers to raise her; she refuses)
Ei non re-spi-ra più! fred-de le
So i-cy to the touch, breath-ing no
(she rises)
(she reels)
membra! Pa-dre mi-o! ca-ro padre! pa-dre a-mato!
long-er! Tell me, fa-ther, that I'm dream-ing! An-swer me, fa-ther!
Vln.
Wind.
Strgs.

(D. Octavio supports her, and leads her to the stone seat)
Don Octavio. (to the servants)
io manco! io moro! Ah! soccor-re-te,a-mi-ci, il mio te-
Have mercy! Vln. Wind. Have pity! Help! Do not stand there gap-ing, but help your
Maestoso.
so-ro! cer-ca-te-mi, re-ca-te-mi qualche o-
mis-tress! Bring smell-ing salts im-me-diate-ly. Go at
Strgs.
maestoso
(A maid-servant hurries into the palace, and returns immediately with a smelling-bottle, which she offers to D. Anna)
Andante.
dor, qual-che spirto! ah non tar-da-te! Donn' Anna! sposa!
once, get some bran-dy. Be quick, I tell you! Donn' An-na! Dear-est!
a-mi-ca! il duolo e-stre-mo la meschi-nella uc-ci-de!
Be-lov-ed! O Grace of Heav-en, let her not die of sor-row!
D. Ann. Don Octavio.
Donna Anna. (with a deep sigh)
Ah! Già rin-vie-ne! da-te-le nuo-vi a-ju-ti. Pa-dre mi-o!
Ah! Look, she's stir-ring! Give her a sip of bran-dy! Let me dream it.
Don Octavio. (to servants)
Ce-la-te, al-lon-ta-na-te agli oc-chi suo-i quel-l'og-get-to d'or-
And quick-ly! Re-move this blood-be-spat-tered bod-y! She mus-n't see it a-

(Serving-men raise the Commandant, and bear him into the palace)
O.
rore! A-ni-ma mi-a, con-so-la-ti!
gain. Wake, Don-na An-na! Be com-fort-ed!
p
p
Allegro.
Donna Anna. (springing up and repulsing Don Octavio as if insane)
O.
A.
fa co-re! Fug-gi, cru-de-le, fug-gi! la-scia, che mora anch'i-o!
I love you! Heart-less tor-men-tor, leave me! Leave_me to die be-side him.
sf Strgs.
p
p
A.
O-ra chè morto, o Di-o! chi a me la vi-ta diè.
Cold is he now and life-less Who gave my life to me.
mf
p
Don Octavio.
O.
Sen-ti, cor mio, deh sen-ti, guar-da-mi un so-lo i-
Hear me, dear heart, Donn' An-na, Turn to_your_faith-ful
O.
stante, ti par-la il ca-ro a-mante, che vi-ve_sol per
lov-er Whose heart is in your keep-ing, O turn your_eyes to_

Donna Anna. (perceiving her error, and giving Don Octavio her hand)

te. Tu sei_ per-don, mio be - ne, l'af - fan - no mi - o, le
me! Once more, let me em - brace _ him. Once more. Once! Fa - ther! My

fp p

(approaching the spot where the Commandant fell)

Don Octavio.

pe - ne. Ah, il pa - dre mio dov' è? Il padre?
fa - ther! But where, O where is he? Donn' An - na,

Vln. cresc.

Lascia, o ca - ra, la ri - membran - za a - ma - ra!
weep no long - er. Time will a - bate your sor - row.

Strgs. Ob. Fag. f fp mf p p

Donna Anna.

hai_ spo - so e pa - dre in me. Ah! il
Both_ hus - band and fa - - ther I'll be. Gone! For -

Fl.

Don Octavio.

pa - dre, il pa - dre mio dov' è? Lascia, o ca - ra,
ev - er! O where, O where is he? Weep no long - er!

cresc. f sfp

O.
La ri-mem-bren-za a-ma-ra! hai spo-so e pa-dre, hai_
Time will a-bate your sor-row. Both hus-band and fa-ther, Both_

mf *p*

(D. Anna, going to the other side, stands with lofty demeanor opposite Don Octavio)

O.
spo-so e pa-dre in me.
hus-band and fa - ther I'll be.

Tutti. *fp* *f*

Donna Anna.

A.
O.
Ah! vendi - car, se il puo - i, giu - ra quel sangue ognor!
Ah! Will you swear to a-venge him? Blood must for blood be poured.

Strgs.

Maestoso. Don Octavio. (raising his hand as for taking an oath)

Lo giu - ro, lo
I swear it. I

O.
giu - ro, lo_ giu - ro a-gli oc-chi_ tuo - i, Lo giu - ro al no- stro a-
swear it. By the eyes I love, I_ swear it. I swear it_ on_ my

Adagio in tempo.

p

Tempo I. Donna Anna.

A.
Che giu - ra - mento, oh
Though cun - ning as the

Don Octavio.

O.
mor! Che giu - ra - mento, oh
sword. Though cun - ning as the

Tempo I.

p *Tutti.* *cresc.*

A. De - i! che bar - ba-ro mo-men-to!
ser - pent He fly from re - tri - bu - tion,

O. De - i! che bar - ba-ro mo-men-to!
ser - pent He fly from re - tri - bu - tion,

Fl. Ob. Fag.
sfp cresc. sfp

A. tra cen-to af-fet - ti e cen-to vammi on-deg-gian - do il cor, tra
Our right-eous wrath shall find him, Blood shall for blood be poured. Our

O. tra cen-to af-fet - ti e cen-to vammi on-deg-gian - do il cor, tra
Our right-eous wrath shall find him, Blood shall for blood be poured. Our

Vln. Cor. Ob. Fag.

A. cen-to af - fet - ti e cen- -to vam-mi on - deg - gian - do il cor.
right-eous wrath shall find him, Blood shall for blood — be poured.

O. cen-to af - fet - ti e cen- -to vam-mi on - deg - gian - do al cor.
right-eous wrath shall find him, Blood shall for blood — be poured.

Winds. Strgs. sfp sfp sf sf p f

A. Ven-di - car quel san - gue, giu - ra!
Blood for blood is — call - ing. Venge-ance!

O. Lo giu - ro a
I swear it! By

p f

O.
gli oc - chi tuo - i, al no - stro a-mor!
love I swear it. I swear it on my sword.
Vlns.
p
p
D. Anna.
A.
Che giu - ra - men - to, oh De - i!
D. Octavio.
No o - cean deep shall hide him
O.
Che giu - ra - men - to, oh De - i!
No o - cean deep shall hide nim
cresc.
fp
A.
che bar - ba-ro mo - men - to! Tra cen - to af - fet - ti e
Nor sub - ter-ra - nean cav-ern; Our right-eous wrath shall
O.
che bar - ba-ro mo - men - to! Tra cen - to af - fet - ti e
Nor sub - ter-ra - nean cav-ern, Our right-eous wrath shall
cresc.
sfp
p
p
A.
cen - to vam-mi on-deg-gian-do il cor, tra cen-to af - fet - ti e
find him, Death be his just re - ward. Our right-eous wrath shall
O.
cen - to vam-mi on-deg-gian-do il cor, tra cen-to af - fet - ti e
find him, Death be his just re - ward. Our right-eous wrath shall

A.
cen- -to vam-mi on-deg - gian - do il cor, vam-mi on - deg-
find him, Death be his just re - ward, his just re -
O.
cen- -to vam-mi on-deg - gian - do il cor,
find him, Death be his just re - ward,
gian - - - - - do, on - deg - gian - do il
ward, his just re -
vam - mi on-deg - gian- - do il cor, vam - mi on - deggian - do il
Death be his just re - ward, Death be his just re -
cresc.
Viola.
cor, vam-mi on-deg - gian- - - - - do, on-deg-
ward, his just re - ward, his
cor, vam - mi on-deg - gian- - do il cor, vam -
ward, Death be his just re - ward, Death
cresc.
gian- - do il cor, vam - mi on - deg - gian- - do il cor,
just re - - ward, Death be his just re - ward,
mi on - deg-gian - do il cor, vam - mi on - deg - gian- - do il cor,
be his just re - ward, Death be his just re - ward,

A.
O.
Vam-mi on - deg - gian - do il cor, vam - mi on - deg - gian-
Death be his just re - ward, Death be his just
Vam-mi on - deg - gian - do il cor, vam - mi on - deg - gian-
Death be his just re - ward, Death be his just
p
- do il cor,
re - ward,
vammi on-deg-gian-do il cor, vam -
Death be his just re - ward, At
- do il cor,
re - ward,
vammi on-deg-gian-do il cor, vam -
Death be his just re - ward, At
f
p
mi on - deggian - do il cor, vam - mi on - deggian - do il cor, on - deg - gian - do il
last his just re-ward, At last his just re-ward, Death his just re -
mi on - deggian - do il cor, vam - mi on - deggian - do il cor, on - deg - gian - do il
last his just re-ward, At last his just re-ward, Death his just re -
cresc.
cor!
ward.
(Exeunt slowly into palace)
cor!
ward.
(Curtain falls rapidly.)
f
f

Scene.— A Street: Early morning.
Don Giovanni, Leporello.
Recit.
Don Giovanni.
Leporello.
Or - sù, spic - cia - ti presto cosa vuo - i? L'af - far, di cui si
Come on, what is your mes-sage? Let me have it! Lis - ten with great at -
Don Giovanni. Leporello. Don Giovanni.
trat - ta, e im - por - tan - te! Lo cre - do. È im - por - tan - tis - si - mo! Meglio an -
ten - tion! It's im - por - tant. I'm lis - tening. I mean it se - rious - ly! I shall
Leporello. D. Giov.
co - ra, fi - ni - sci - la! Giu - ra - te di non an - dar in col - le - ra! Lo
lis - ten with grav - i - ty. You prom - ise me that you will not get fu - rious? Yes,
Leporello.
giuro sul mio o - nore, pur - chè non par - li del Com - men - da - to - re. Sia - mo
yes, but on con - di - tion it's not to do with the Com - men - da - to - re. No one's
Don Giovanni. Leporello. Don Giov. Leporello.
so - li? Lo ve - do! Nes - sun ci sen - te? Via! Vi pos - so di - re
look - ing? Of course not. No one's in ear - shot? No. And I'm al - lowed to
D. G. Leporello.
tut - to li - be - ra - mente? Sì! Dunque quand'è co - sì Ca - ro Si - gnor pa - dro - ne, La
speak with ab - so - lute frank - ness? Yes. Ver - y well, it is this: if you con - tin - ue lead - ing this
(shouts in his ear.) Don Giovanni.
vi - ta che me - na - te è da bricco - ne! Te - me - ra - rio, in tal gui - sa!
kind of life much long - er You'll go to Hell, sir! You damned scoun - drel! But how dare you!
Leporello. Don Giovanni.
E il giu - ra - men - to! Non sò di giu - ra - men - ti; ta - ci, o
Now, now, you prom - ised. To hell with what I prom - ised. Si - lence... or

Leporello.
Don Giovanni.
G.
L.
ch'io— Non par-lo più, non fia - to o pa - dron mi - o! Co - sì sa - re - mo a -
else ... I'll nev-er speak. Not e - ven in a whis-per. Be good and I'll for -
Leporello.
mi - ci, or o - di un po - co! sai tu per-chè son qui? Non, ne sò
give you. Let's change the sub - ject. Why do you think I'm here? I nev - er
nulla! ma es-sendo l'al - ba chiara, non sa-reb-be qualche nuo-va conquista? io lo
think, sir. So ear-ly in the morn-ing could the rea-son be some charm-ing ad-ven-ture? For the
Don Giovanni.
de - vo sa - per, per por-la in lis - ta! Va là, che sei il grand'uom! Sap-pi ch'io
sake of our list you'll have to tell me. That's bet - ter, that's more like my Le - po -
so - no in-na-mora - to d'u - na bel - la Da - ma, e son cer - to che m'a - ma;
rel- lo. It is an-oth - er love-ly lit - tle crea-ture, and I know that she loves me.
la vi - di, le parla - i, me-co al ca-si - no questa not-te ver - rà: Zit - to! mi pare
I've met her. We have spok-en, and she has promised she will meet me to-night. Ah, how de-li-cious!
Leporello.
sen-tir o - dor di fem-mi-na! (Co - spet-to, che o-do - ra - to per-fet - to!)
That scent is, sure - ly, fem - i - nine. For wom-en you've a nose like a blood-hound!
Don Giovanni.
Leporello.
Al - l'a - ria, mi par bel - la. (E che oc - chio! di - co!)
From here I'd say she's pret - ty. And an ea - gle's eye-sight.

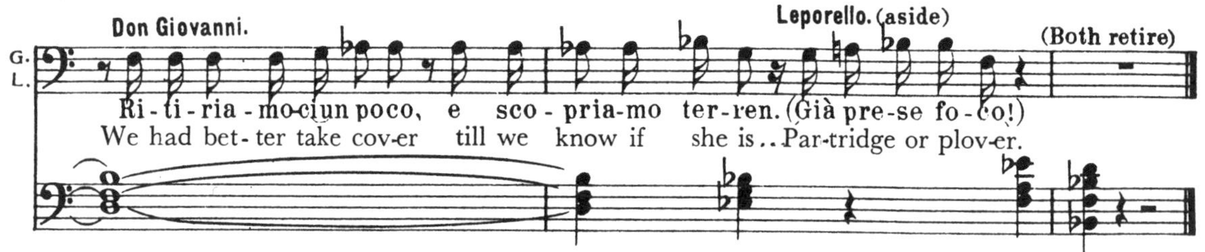

Don Giovanni.
G.
L.
Leporello. (aside)
(Both retire)
Ri-ti-ria-mo ci un poco, e sco-pria-mo ter-ren. (Già pre-se fo-co!)
We had bet-ter take cov-er till we know if she is.. Par-tridge or plov-er.

№ 3. "Ah! chi mi dice mai."
Trio.

Donna Elvira (in a travelling-dress); Don Giovanni, and Leporello.

Allegro.

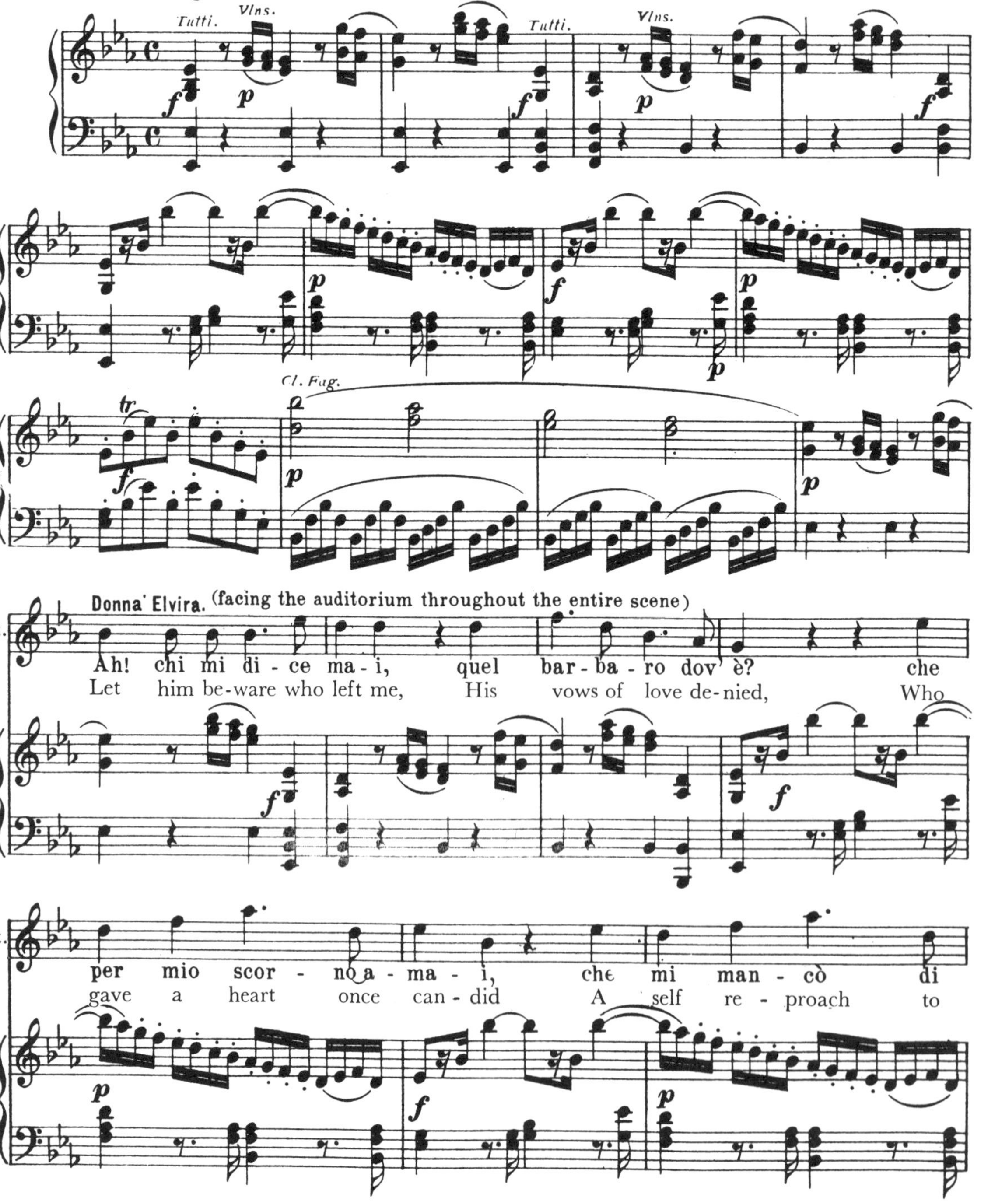

Tutti.
Vlns.
Tutti.
Vlns.
Cl. Fag.
Donna Elvira. (facing the auditorium throughout the entire scene)
E.
Ah! chi mi di-ce ma-i, quel bar-ba-ro dov' è? che
Let him be-ware who left me, His vows of love de-nied, Who
E.
per mio scor-no a-ma-i, che mi man-cò di
gave a heart once can-did A self re-proach to

E.
fè? che mi man-cò di fè?
hide— Sor - - - - row and shame to hide.
cresc.
sf
sfp
(D. Giovanni and Leporello reappear)
Ah! se ri-tro- -vo l'empio,
No more shall they be hid-den,
sfp
sfp
sfp
(Leporello busies himself with Don Giovanni's attire, helps him draw on
e a me non tor- -na an-cor, vo'
Now shame-less I have sworn, Di-
sfp
sfp
cresc.
his gloves, etc.)
far- -ne or-ren- -do scem- -pio, gli
rect - - - ly I'll de-nounce him. And
fp
fp
fp
fp
vo' ca-var il cor, gli vo' ca-var il
make him bear the scorn That I a-lone have
fp
fp
f
f

Don Giovanni. (to Leporello)
E.
G.
cor! U - di - sti? qualche bel - la, dal_ va - go ab - ban - do -
borne. She's troub-led. Could some bad man have_ left a girl so
p
Donna Elvira.
G.
E.
na - ta? Vo' far - ne or - ren - do scem - pio, gli
love-ly? My rage, I swear, shall make him Re -
fp
Don Giovanni. (with contemptuous pity)
E.
G.
vo' ca-var il cor! Po - ve - ri - na! Po - ve - ri - na!
gret that he was born... How she suf-fers! How she suf-fers!
fp
p
Donna Elvira.
E.
Gli vo' ca - var il_ cor, sì, gli vo' ca - var il_
That he was ev - er_ born! Ah! That he was ev - er_
f
p
Don Giovanni. (to Leporello)
Leporello. (aside)
E.
G.
L.
cor! Cerchiam di con-so - la - re il suo tor - men-to. Co - sì ne con-so -
born! We ought to try to bring her con - so - la-tion. The girls you have con-
p

Donna Elvira.
L.
E.
lò mil-le e ot-to cen-to.
soled would make a na-tion.
Ah! chi mi di-ce
Why did you lie and
f
p
(Leporello steals about Donna Elvira to catch sight of her face; unsuccessful, he informs his
ma-i, quel bar-ba-ro dov' è? che per mio scor-no a-
leave me? Where, trai-tor, have you run? Come back and I'll for-
master pantomimically of his failure)
ma-i, che mi man-cò di fè? che
give you The harm that you have done, What-
cresc.
mi man-cò di fè?
ev-er wrong you've done.
sfp
Ah, se ri-tro-vo l'em-pio,
But if you still are faith-less,

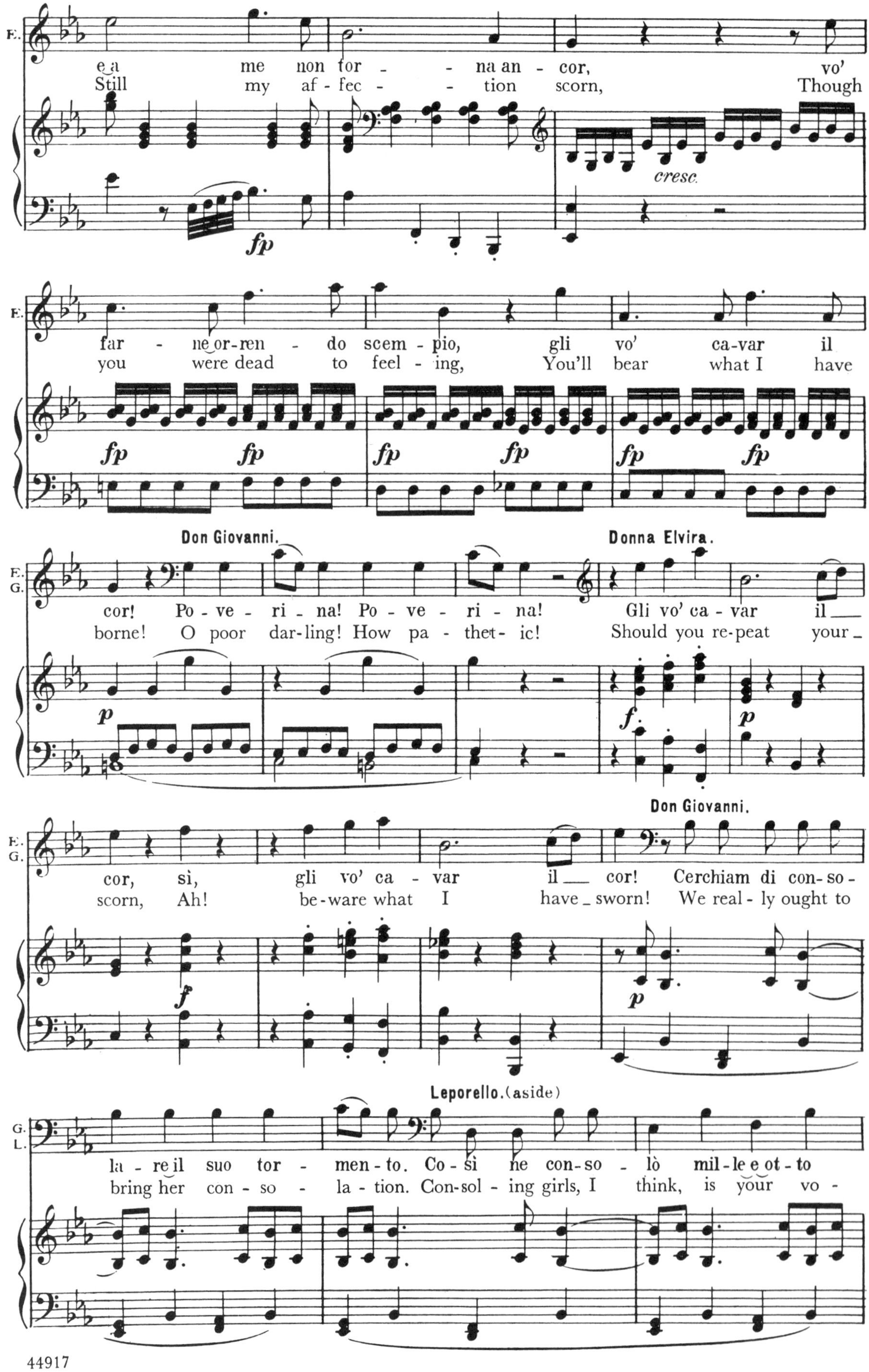
e a me non tor - na an - cor, vo'
Still my af - fec - tion scorn, Though
cresc.
fp
far - ne or - ren - do scem - pio, gli vo' ca - var il
you were dead to feel - ing, You'll bear what I have
fp fp fp fp fp fp
Don Giovanni.
Donna Elvira.
cor! Po - ve - ri - na! Po - ve - ri - na! Gli vo' ca - var il
borne! O poor dar - ling! How pa - thet - ic! Should you re - peat your
p f p
Don Giovanni.
cor, sì, gli vo' ca - var il cor! Cerchiam di con - so -
scorn, Ah! be - ware what I have sworn! We real - ly ought to
f p
Leporello. (aside)
la - re il suo tor - men - to. Co - sì ne con - so - lò mil - le e ot - to
bring her con - so - la - tion. Con - sol - ing girls, I think, is your vo -

Donna Elvira.
E.
Gli vo' ca-va - - - - - re il cor, gli vo' ca-va-
You'll bear what I have — borne, You'll bear what I
L.
cen-to.
ca-tion.
f
p
(Don Giovanni clears his throat several times, to attract
- - - - - - - re il cor, gli
have — borne, You'll
Donna Elvira's notice; she does not hear him, but grows more and more excited. Finally his patience
vo' cavar il cor, ca - - var il
bear what I have borne, What I have
cresc.
gives way, and he steps up to Donna Elvira boldly, but politely.)
Don Giovanni.
(raising his hat)
D. Elvira.
E. G.
cor! Si - gno - ri - na! Si - gno - ri - na! Chi è
borne. Gra-cious la-dy, Gra-cious la - dy, Who's

Recit.
Don Giovanni. (starting back; mezza voce)
Leporello. (aside)
Donna Elvira. (indignantly)
E. G. L.
là? Stel-le! che ve-do! O bel-la! Don-na El-vi-ra! Don Gio-
that? (Well, of all peo-ple!) (How per-fect! Donn' El-vi-ra!) Don Gio-
Leporello. (aside)
E. L.
van-ni! sei qui? mostro! fel-lon! ni-do d'in-ganni! Che ti-to-li cruscan-ti!
van-ni! It's you, treacherous beast, poi-son-ous ser-pent! (A flat-ter-ing de-scrip-tion!
Don Giovanni.
L. G.
man-co ma-le che lo co-no-sce be-ne. Via, ca-ra Donna El-
One would think she knew him as well as I do.) Now, dear, dear, Donn' El-
G.
vi-ra, cal-ma-te que-sta col-le-ra! sen-ti-te, la-
vi-ra, con-trol your-self, be sen-si-ble and lis-ten. Al-
Donna Elvira.
G. E.
scia-te-mi par-lar! Co-sa puoi di-re, do-po a-zion si ne-ra? In ca-sa
low me to ex-plain. Noth-ing you say can jus-ti-fy your ac-tions. Did you not
E.
mi-a en-tri fur-ti-va-men-te, a for-za d'ar-te, di giu-ramen-ti, e
worm your way in-to my af-fec-tions? Did you not court me . . . with sighs and vows of
E.
di lu-sin-ghe ar-ri-vi a se-dur-re il cor mi-o; m'in-na-
ev-er-last-ing de-vo-tion? Till my pure heart be-lieved you and, a-

E.
mo - ri, o cru-de - le! mi di - chia - ri tua spo - sa, e poi, man -
las, came to love you. First you prom-ised me mar - riage ... and then de -
E.
can-do del - la ter-ra e del ciel al san - to drit-to, con e-nor - me de-lit - to
ny-ing ... ev -'ry tie, ev -'ry law of earth and Heav-en ... with in-cred - i-ble base-ness,
E.
do - po tre dì da Bur-gos t'al - lon - ta - ni, m'ab-ban-do - ni, mi
aft- er three days .... you stole a - way from Bur-gos ... You for-sook me ... You
E.
fug - gi, e la-sci in pre - da al ri - mor - so ed al pian - to per pe-na for - se
van-ished ... And I was left to re-morse and vain re - pent-ance. Dear must I pay for
Leporello (aside)
Don Giovanni.
E.
L.
G.
che t'a-mai co-tan - to. (Pa - re un li - bro stam-pa - to!) Oh in quanto a que-sto
lov - ing you so dear - ly! (She's been read-ing ro - man-ces!) For var-ious rea-sons
(to Leporello)
Leporello. (ironically)
G.
L.
eb - bi le mie ra - gio - ni! è ve - ro? È ve - ro!
I was ob - liged to do it. (As you know.) (As I know.)
Donna Elvira. (to Don Giovanni)
L.
E.
e che ra - gio - ni for - ti! E qua - li so - no, se non la tua per -
Ver - y im - por - tant rea-sons. Too well I know them. Your shame-less love of

E.
fi - dia, la leg-ge - rez-za tu - a? Ma il giu - sto cie - lo vol - le ch'io ti tro -
ly - ing, your ut-ter lack of feel-ing. The right - eous hand of Heav-en has led me

E. G.
Don Giovanni.
vas - si, per far le sue, le mie ven - det-te. Eh vi - a, sia - te più ra - gio -
hith-er. And for your mis-deeds you shall an-swer. O come, now, come, you are talk-ing

G.
ne - vo - le: (mi po-ne a ci-men-to co - stei.) se non cre-de-te al lab - bro
fool - ish-ly. (We're in for a dif - fi - cult scene.) Since you re-fuse to hear what

G. L.
Leporello. D.Giov. (to Lep. aloud)
mi - o, cre - de - te a que-sto ga-lant - uo - mo. (Sal-vo il ve - ro.) Via, dil-le un
I say, this hon-est fel-low shall speak for me. (Trust me, La-dy!) You tell this

G. L. E.
Leporello. (aside to Don Giovanni) Don Giovanni. (aloud) D. Elv. (to Lep.)
po - co. (E co - sa de - vo dir - le?) Sì, sì, dil - le pur tut - to. Eb -
la - dy. (But what am I to tell her?) You tell her the whole sto - ry. The

E. L.
(Don Giovanni escapes.) Leporello.
ben, fa pre - sto! Ma - da - ma, ve - ra - men - te, in que - sto
truth! No ly - ing! Dear la - dy . . . to speak frank-ly . . . the world we

L. E.
Donna Elvira.
mon-do con-cio - sia co - sa quan-do fos - se che Il quadro non è ton-do! Scia - gu -
live in . . . is, as you know, a vale of sor-row where a square is not a cir-cle. O you

E.
(Turning as if to Don Giovanni)
ra - to! Co - sì del mio do - lor gio - co ti pren - di? Ah
cow-ard! How dare you mock a poor de - fense - less wom - an! And

Leporello.
E.
L.
voi! stel-le! l'i-ni-quo fug-gì! mi-se-ra me! do-ve? in qual par-te? Eh, la-
you van-ished! The vil-lain has fled, stol-en a-way! But where? Which di-rec-tion? Down! Be
Donna Elvira.
L.
E.
scia-te che va-da; e-gli non mer-ta che di lui ci pen-sia-te. Il scel-le-
glad that he has-n't tak-en you with him; and for-get that you know him. How can I
Leporello. (Donna Elvira turns to the bench before the house, and seats herself sadly.)
E.
L.
ra-to m'in-gan-no, mi tra-dì! Eh, con-so-la-te-vi! non sie-te
do it, how for-get his de-ceit? Ma-dam, con-sole your-self: You're not the
L.
voi, non fo-ste, e non sa-re-te nè la pri-ma, nè
first, be-lieve me, to be his vic-tim, nor will you be the
(Leporello takes out a book, or a long, narrow roll of paper, covered with silhouettes and names.)
L.
l'ul-ti-ma; guar-da-te, que-sto non pic-ciol li-bro è tut-to
last of them. I pray you glance at this leng-thy vol-ume con-tain-ing
L.
pie-no dei no-mi di sue bel-le; O-gni vil-la, o-gni bor-go, o-gni pa-
all of the names of those he's con-quered, their de-scrip-tions, with the dates and hours and lo-
L.
e-se, È te-sti-mon di sue don-ne-sche im-pre-se.
ca-tions of his wide-spread, in-ti-mate re-cre-a-tions.

Nº 4. "Madamina."

Aria.

L.
in Al - ma-gna due cen-to e trent' u - na,
Down for Eng-land, a hun - dred-e - lev - en;
p
f
3
L.
cen - to in Francia, in Turchia no-vant' u-na; ma, in I -
For San Ma-ri-no a mere nine-ty-sev-en; But prim and
p
fp
L.
spa-gna, ma in I - spa-gna son già mille e tre! mil-le e tre!
prop-er Spain con - tri-butes a thou-sand-and-three! Can that be?
p
sfp
Vlns.
Tutti
p
L.
mil - le e tre! V'han fra que-ste con-ta - di - ne,
Yes, it's three. There are bar-maids, bas-ket-weav-ers,
L.
ca- me-rie - re, cit - ta - di - ne, V'han contesse, ba - ro - nes - se,
There are dair-y-maids and di-vas, Count-less count-ess-es, prin-cess-es,

L.
marchesa - ne, prin-ci - pesse, e v'han don-ne d'o - gni gra-do, d'o-gni for-ma, d'ogni e-
In the ranks of his suc-cess-es, Ev-'ry pos - si - ble con - di-tion, Oc-cu-pa-tion, form and
cresc.
tà, d'o - gni for-ma, d'o-gni e-tà, In I - ta-li-a
age All a - rouse his gal-lant-rage! In A - ra - bi - a,
f
p
Vln.
Cello & Bass
sei cen-to e qua-ran - ta, in Al-ma-gna
ten doz-en were fool-ish; In Dal-ma-tia,
due cen-to e trent' u - na, cen - to in Fran - cia, in Tur-
a hun-dred were wan-ton; Here's Hel - ve - tia— a
chia no - vant' u - na, ma, ma, ma in I - spa - gna! ma in I -
gross in each Can-ton; But, but, but o-ver-prud - ish Spain con-

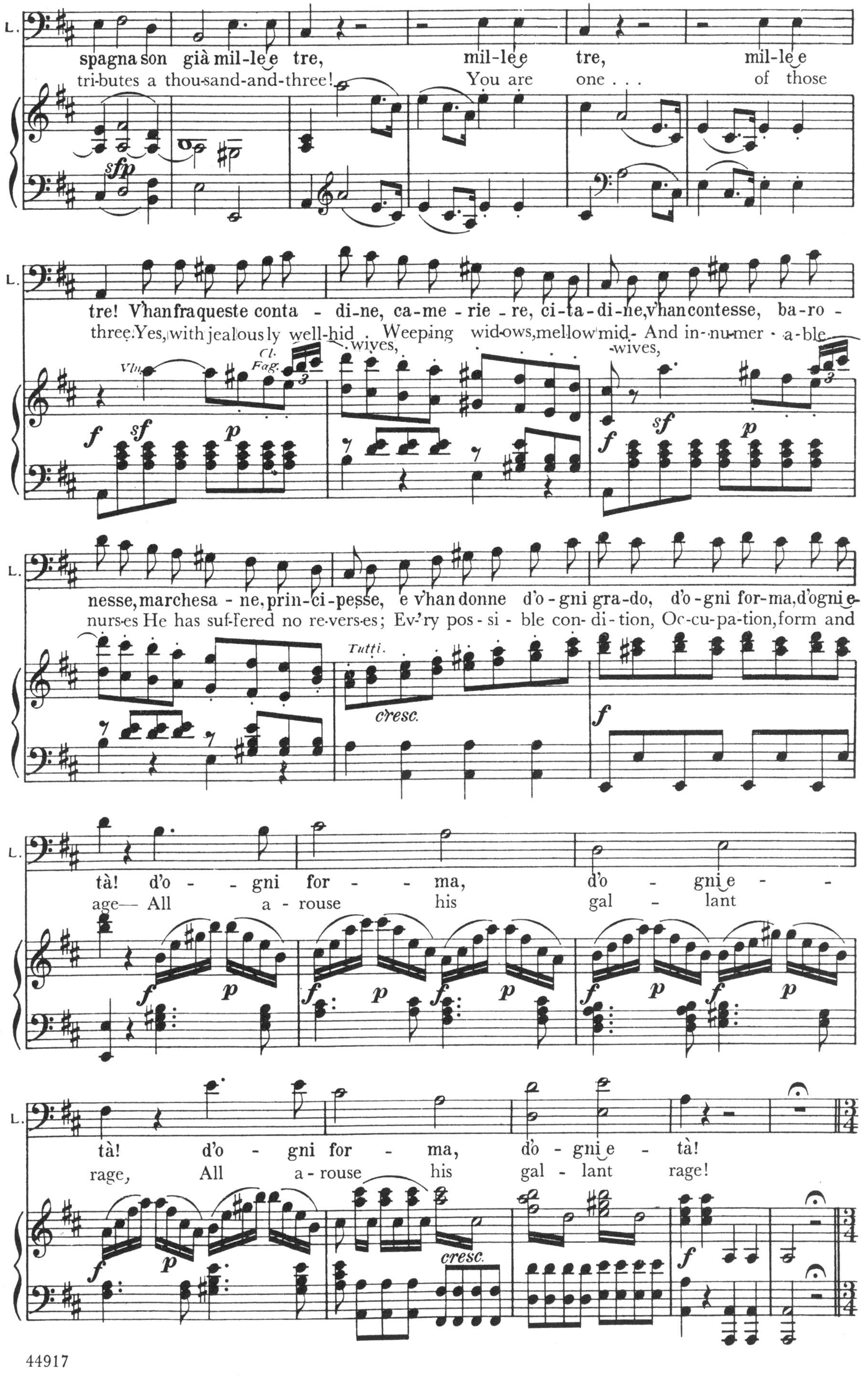
L.
spagna son già mil-le e tre, mil-le e tre, mil-le e
tri-butes a thou-sand-and-three! You are one . . . of those
sfp
tre! V'han fra queste conta - di-ne, ca-me - rie - re, ci-ta-di-ne, v'han contesse, ba-ro -
three. Yes, with jealous-ly well-hid wives, Weeping wid-ows, mellow mid-wives, And in-numer - a-ble
Vln.
Cl. Fag.
f sf p
nesse, marchesa - ne, prin-ci-pesse, e v'han donne d'o-gni gra-do, d'o-gni for-ma, d'ogni e-
nurs-es He has suf-fered no re-vers-es; Ev'ry pos-si - ble con-di - tion, Oc-cu-pa-tion, form and
Tutti.
cresc.
tà! d'o - gni for - ma, d'o - gni e -
age— All a - rouse his gal - lant
tà! d'o - gni for - ma, d'o - gni e - tà!
rage, All a - rouse his gal - lant rage!
cresc.

Andante con moto.
L.
Nel - la bionda e - gli ha l'u - san-za di lo - dar - la
All the prais-es with which he courts them Fol - low or - ders
Str.
p
Fl.
fp
la gen-ti - lez - za, nel - la bru - na la co -
where-by he sorts them: Blondes are mod - est, dark ones
Tutti
Cor.
f
stanza, nel - la bian - ca la dol - cez - za.
gra-cious, Red - heads can - did, white sa - ga - cious.
Str.
p
Fl. Fag. Vln.
Vuol d'in-ver - no la grassot - ta, vuol d'e-sta - te la ma -
Bulk at-tracts him dur-ing win - ter, Dur-ing sum - mer, more the
cresc.
grotta, e la gran - de ma - e -
splin-ter. He will woo them tall and
f
p
f
p

L.
sto - sa, e la gran - de ma - e -
flor - id, Sport - ing clouds a - bout the
f
p
cresc.
L.
sto - - - - - - sa. La pic - ci - na, la pic -
fore - - - - - - head; He will woo them Tee-ny-
f
Fl. Ob.
Bassi
p
Vln.
Fl. Ob.
Bassi
L.
ci - na, la pic - ci - na, la pic - ci - na, la pic - ci - na, la pic -
ti - ny, tee - ny- ti - ny, tee - ny- ti - ny, tee - ny- ti - ny, tee - ny-
Ob.
Fl.
Vln.
Fag.
Bassi
L.
ci-na, la pic-ci-na, la picci-na, la pic - ci - na è ognor vez - zo - sa, è ognor vez -
ti-ny, tee-ny- ti-ny, tee-ny- ti-ny, Tee-ny- ti - ny, of bare-ly bean- size And in all
Tutti
p
L.
zo - sa, è ognor vez - zo - sa; del - le vecchie fa con - qui - sta
man - ner of in - be - tween-size. Ripe du - en - nas he has con-tent - ed
p
fp

L.
pel pia - cer_ di por - le in li - sta, sua passion pre - do - mi -
That his _ list Might be some - what aug - ment - ed; But the most - of - all he
p
Fag.
L.
nan - te_ è la gio - vin prin - ci - pian - te;
sa - vors_ Un - in - i - ti - at - ed fa - vors.
Fl.
Fag.
Vln.
L.
non si pic - ca, se sia ric - ca, se sia brut - ta, se sia
Ill or health - y, Poor or wealth - y, Plain or pret - ty, Dull or
tr
cresc.
L.
bel - la, se sia ric - ca, brut - ta, se sia bel - la, pur - chè_
wit - ty, High - born, low - ly, Scrag - gy hags or beau - ties, Be they_
tr
Ob.
Vln.
p
L.
por - ti la_ gon - nel - la, voi sa - pe - te
fe - male, they're_ his du - ties— How he meets them,

L.
quel che fa, voi sa - pe - te quel che
this can show, How he greets them, this can
Fl.
Fag.
L.
fa, pur che por - ti la gon - nel - la, voi sa - pe - te quel che
show. Be they fe - male, they're his du - ties In a serv - ice that you
Vln.
L.
fa, voi sa - pe - te, voi sa - pe - te quel che fa,
know, In a serv - ice, In a serv - ice that you know.
Ob. Vln.
Fl.
Fag.
mf
p
L.
quel che fa, quel che fa, voi sa -
This can show That you know, In a
f
f
L.
pe - te quel che fa.
serv - ice that you know.
(Exit hastily into villa.)

Recit.

Donna Elvira. (alone)

In que-sta for-ma dun-que mi tra-dì il scel-le-ra-to! è questo il
To think my love was yield-ed, not to love or de-sire, but to ob-

pre-mio che quel bar-ba-ro ren-de all' a-mor mi-o! Ah, ven-di-car vo-
ses-sion! That is worse than I ev-er had im-ag-ined. Venge-ance a-lone he

gl'i-o l'in-gan-na-to mio cor! pria ch'ei mi fug-ga, si ri-cor-ra, si
mer-its! And I'd felt that my love gave me a pow-er sent by Heav-en to

(Exit into the house.)

va-da; io sento in pet-to sol ven-det-ta par-lar, rab-bia e dispet-to!
save him, although he left me. I shall love him no more; nev-er shall I weak-en!

Nº 5. "Giovinette, che fate all' amore."

Duet and Chorus.

Scene. — The open Country.

Zerlina, Masetto, and Chorus of Villagers, dancing and singing.

(turning to the maidens, who press about her, while Masetto, on the other side, is surrounded by the lads.)
Zerlina.
Z.
Gio-vi - net - te, che fa-te all'a - mo - re, che fa-te all' a - mo - re, non la -
Pret-ty maid with your grac-es a - dorn-ing the dew-span-gled morn-ing, The red
Str.
p
Fl.
Ob.
Fag.
scia-te, che pas-si l'e - tà, che pas-si l'e - tà, che pas-si l'e - tà! Se nel
rose and the white fade a - way, Both with-er a - way, All fade in a day. Of your
se - no vi bu - li - ca il co - re, vi bu - li - ca il co - re, il ri -
pride and un - kind - ness re - lent - ing, to kiss - es con - sent - ing, All the
me - dio ve - de - te - lo quà! che pia -
pains of your shep-herd al - lay, As the
cer, che piacer che sa - rà!
cuck-oo flies o - ver the may.
(the maidens form a ring, and dance around Zerlina.)
Chorus. SOPRANO & ALTO.
Ah! che pia - cer, che pia-cer che sa -
Ah! As the cuck - oo flies o - ver the
Tutti.
f

Masetto. (to the lads.)
M.
Gio-vi-net-ti leg-gieri di
What is youth-ful de-sire but a
rà, la-la-re-la-la, la-la-re-la-la!
may. Fa la la la la. Fa la la la la.
sf p
sf p
f
Str.
p
te-sta, leg-gie-ri di te-sta, non an-da-te gi-ran-do di quà e là e
feath-er that veers with the weath-er, But a fan-cy that wan-ders a-stray, This way, that
là, e quà e là; po-co du-ra de' mat-ti la fe-sta, de' mat-ti la
way, This way, that way? Then if one from the day of their meet-ing Stay true to his
fe-sta, ma per me co-min-cia-to non ha, co-min-cia-to non
sweet-ing, Let us crown them with lau-rel and bay: With a-ho and a-
ha! che pia-cer, che piacer che sa-rà!
heigh, As the cuck-oo flies o-ver the may.
Chorus. TENOR & BASS.
(ring and dance)
Tutti
Ah
Ah
f

che pia - cer, che pia - cer che sa - rà; la - la - re - la - la, la - la - re - la -
As the cuck - oo flies o - ver the may. Fa la la la la Fa la la la

(Zerlina and Masetto leave the groups and advance to centre, where the young chorus forms a great ring around them.)

Zerlina.

Vie - ni, vie - ni ca - ri - no, go - dia - mo, e can - tiamo, e bal - liamo, e suo -
Let us turn, let us twist with a mo - tion, Quick and live - ly as fish in the

Masetto.

Vie - ni, vie - ni ca - ri - no, go - dia - mo, e can - tiamo, e bal - liamo, e suo -
Let us turn, let us twist with a mo - tion, Quick and live - ly as fish in the

la!
la.

Vln.

sf *p*

nia - mo, vie - ni, vie - ni ca - ri - no, go - dia - mo, che pia - cer, che pia - cer che sa -
o - cean, The two halves of a sin - gle de - vo - tion, As the cuck - oo flies o - ver the

nia - mo, vie - ni, vie - ni ca - ri - no, go - dia - mo, che pia - cer, che pia - cer che sa -
o - cean, The two halves of a sin - gle de - vo - tion, As the cuck - oo flies o - ver the

rà! Ah! che pia - cer, che pia - cer che sa -
may. Ah! As the cuck - oo flies o - ver the

rà! Ah! che pia - cer, che pia - cer che sa -
may. Ah! As the cuck - oo flies o - ver the

Z.
rà!
may.
M.
rà!
may.
(D. Giovanni and Leporello come out of the villa; both stop to look on.)
SOPR. & ALTO.
Chorus.
Ah, che pia - cer, che pia-cer che sa -
Ah! As the cuck-oo flies o - ver the
TENOR & BASS.
Ah, che pia - cer, che pia-cer che sa -
Ah! As the cuck-oo flies o - ver the
rà! La - la - re - la - la, re - la - la, re - la - la, la - la - re - la -
may. Fa la la la la la la la la la la Fa la la la
la, re-la - la, re-la - la!
la la la la la la la.

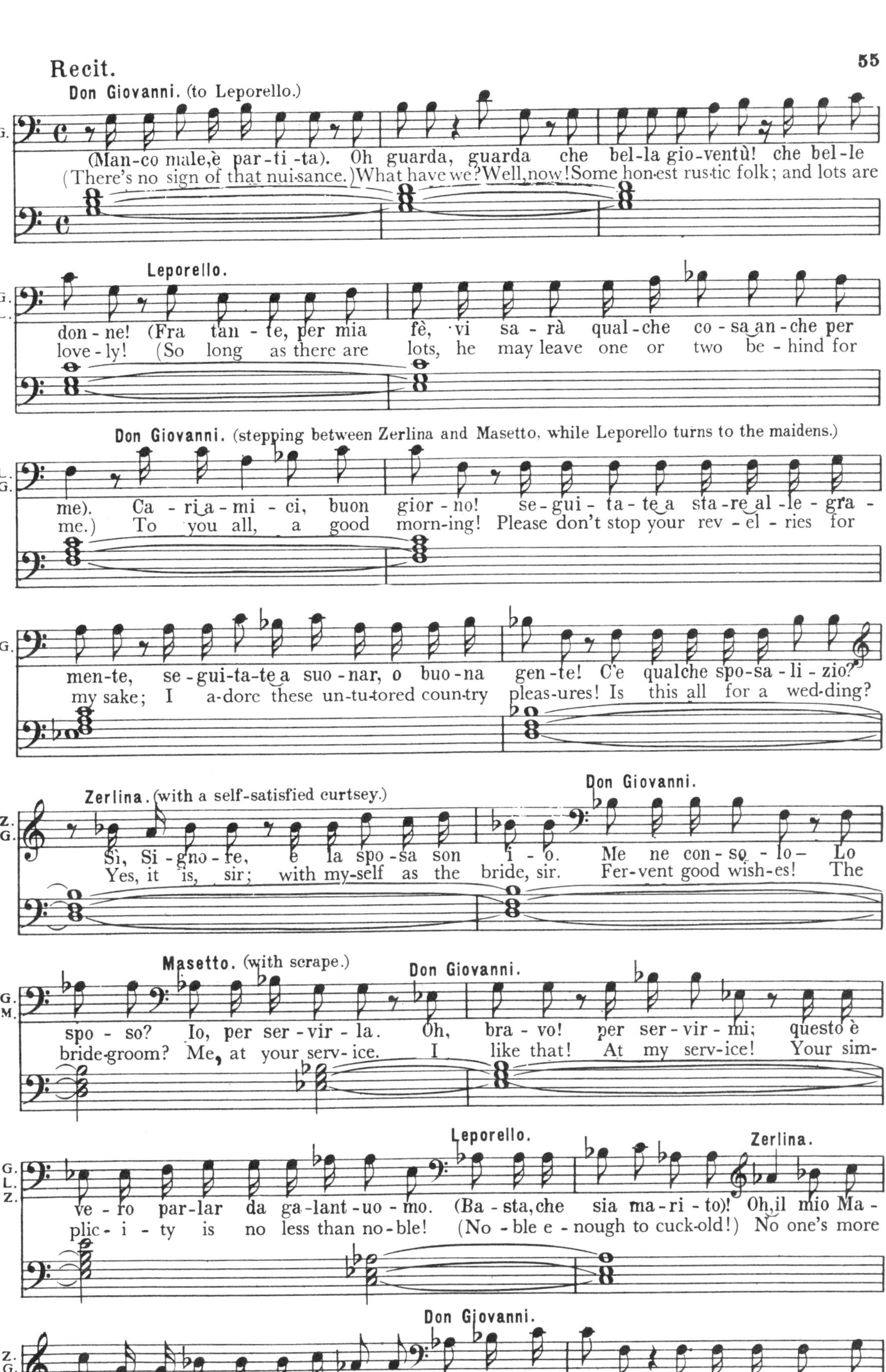
Recit.
Don Giovanni. (to Leporello.)
(Man-co male,è par-ti-ta). Oh guarda, guarda che bel-la gio-ventù! che bel-le
(There's no sign of that nui-sance.) What have we? Well, now! Some hon-est rus-tic folk; and lots are
Leporello.
don-ne! (Fra tan-te, per mia fè, vi sa-rà qual-che co-sa an-che per
love-ly! (So long as there are lots, he may leave one or two be-hind for
Don Giovanni. (stepping between Zerlina and Masetto, while Leporello turns to the maidens.)
me). Ca-ri a-mi-ci, buon gior-no! se-gui-ta-te a sta-re al-le-gra-
me.) To you all, a good morn-ing! Please don't stop your rev-el-ries for
men-te, se-gui-ta-te a suo-nar, o buo-na gen-te! C'è qualche spo-sa-li-zio?
my sake; I a-dore these un-tu-tored coun-try pleas-ures! Is this all for a wed-ding?
Zerlina. (with a self-satisfied curtsey.)
Sì, Si-gno-re, e la spo-sa son i-o.
Yes, it is, sir; with my-self as the bride, sir.
Don Giovanni.
Me ne con-so-lo- Lo
Fer-vent good wish-es! The
Masetto. (with scrape.)
spo-so? Io, per ser-vir-la.
bride-groom? Me, at your serv-ice.
Don Giovanni.
Oh, bra-vo! per ser-vir-mi; questo è
I like that! At my serv-ice! Your sim-
ve-ro par-lar da ga-lant-uo-mo.
plic-i-ty is no less than no-ble!
Leporello.
(Ba-sta, che sia ma-ri-to)!
(No-ble e-nough to cuck-old!)
Zerlina.
Oh, il mio Ma-set-to è un uom d'ot-ti-mo co-re.
No one's more gen-er-ous than my dear Ma-set-to.
Don Giovanni.
Oh anch'io, ve-de-te! vo-glio che sia-mo a-
What could be bet-ter! Let us be friends for-

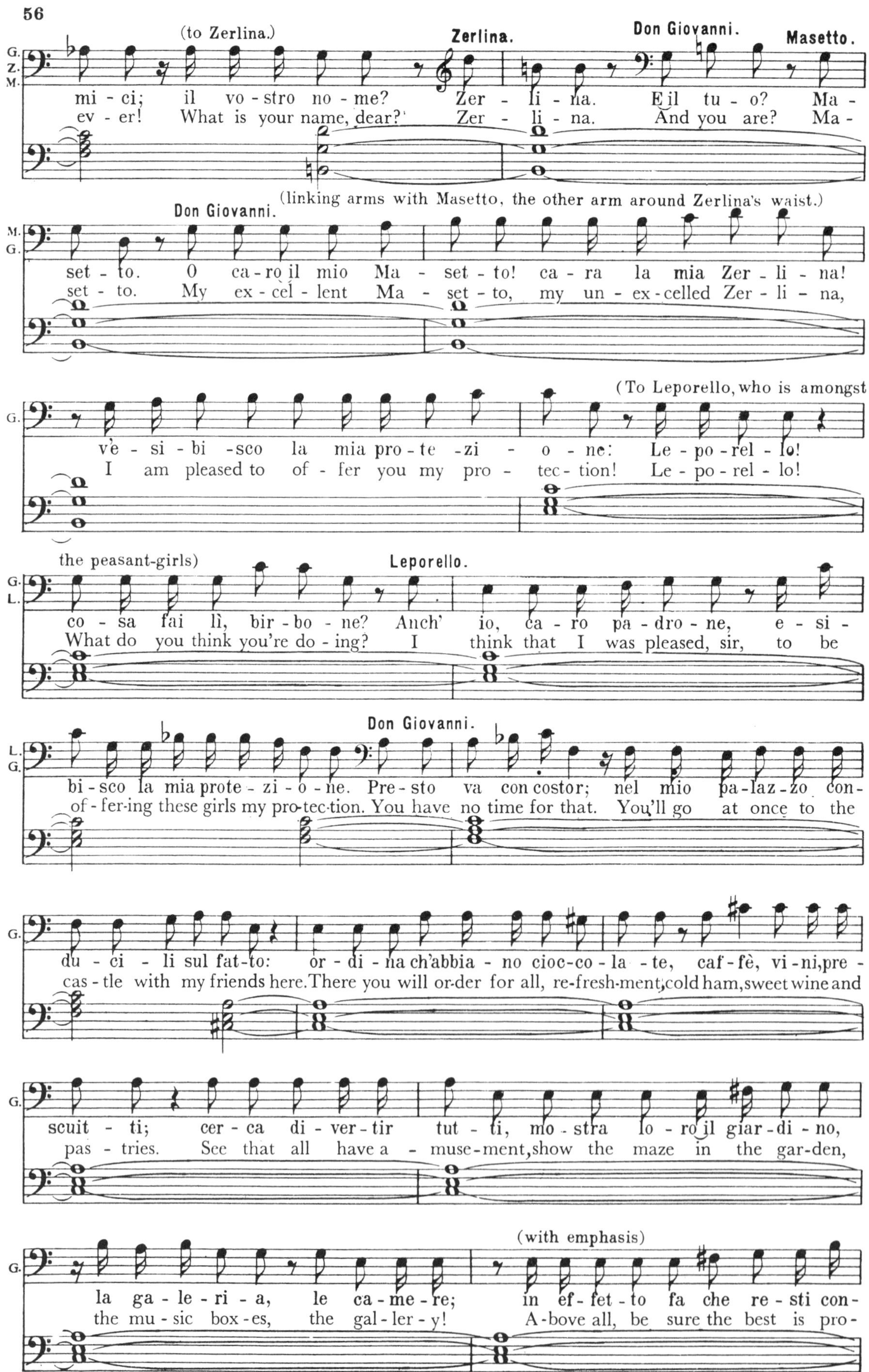
(to Zerlina.)
Zerlina.
Don Giovanni.
Masetto.
G.
Z.
M.
mi - ci; il vo - stro no - me? Zer - li - na. E il tu - o? Ma -
ev - er! What is your name, dear? Zer - li - na. And you are? Ma -
Don Giovanni.
(linking arms with Masetto, the other arm around Zerlina's waist.)
M.
G.
set - to. O ca - ro il mio Ma - set - to! ca - ra la mia Zer - li - na!
set - to. My ex - cel - lent Ma - set - to, my un - ex - celled Zer - li - na,
G.
(To Leporello, who is amongst
vè - si - bi - sco la mia pro - te - zi - o - ne: Le - po - rel - lo!
I am pleased to of - fer you my pro - tec - tion! Le - po - rel - lo!
the peasant-girls)
Leporello.
G.
L.
co - sa fai lì, bir - bo - ne? Anch' io, ca - ro pa - dro - ne, e - si -
What do you think you're do - ing? I think that I was pleased, sir, to be
Don Giovanni.
L.
G.
bi - sco la mia prote - zi - o - ne. Pre - sto va con costor; nel mio pa - laz - zo con -
of - fer - ing these girls my pro - tec - tion. You have no time for that. You'll go at once to the
G.
du - ci - li sul fat - to: or - di - na ch'abbia - no cioc - co - la - te, caf - fè, vi - ni, pre -
cas - tle with my friends here. There you will or - der for all, re - fresh - ment, cold ham, sweet wine and
G.
scuit - ti; cer - ca di - ver - tir tut - ti, mo - stra lo - ro il giar - di - no,
pas - tries. See that all have a - muse - ment, show the maze in the gar - den,
(with emphasis)
G.
la ga - le - ri - a, le ca - me - re; in ef - fet - to fa che re - sti con -
the mu - sic box - es, the gal - ler - y! A - bove all, be sure the best is pro -

(pokes Leporello in the ribs.)
Leporello.
(to the villagers.)
Masetto.
Don Giovanni.
G. L. M.
ten-to il mio Ma-set-to, hai ca-pi-to? Ho ca-pi-to; an-diam. Si-gno-re! Co-sa
vid-ed for Ma-set-to! Do you fol-low? Like a shad-ow. We're off... My lord-ship. You're still
Masetto.
(While the rest enter the inn. Don Giov. detains Zerlina.)
Leporello. (to Masetto.)
G. M. L.
c'è? La Zer-li-na sen-za me non può star. In vostro lo-co ci sa-rà sua Eccel-
here? But I can-not leave Zer-li-na a-lone. Have you for-got-ten your most no-ble pro-
L. G.
len-za, e sa-prà be-ne fa-re le vo-stri par-ti.
Don Giovanni.
Oh, la Zer-
tec-tor? Be sure he will pro-tect her in your place no-bly. Pre-cious Zer-
G. Z.
li-na è in man d'un Ca-va-lier; va pur, fra po-co el-la me-co ver-rà.
Zerlina.
Va!
li-na will be my spe-cial care. My word. I think that will more than suf-fice. Please!
Z. M.
non te-me-re! nel-le ma-ni son io d'un Ca-va-lie-re.
Masetto.
E per que-sto?
You must go now. In a no-ble-man's hands, what harm can touch me? Must I tell you?
Zerlina.
Masetto.
(trying to take her hand.)
Don Giov.
Z. M. G.
E per que-sto non c'è da du-bi-tar. Ed io, co-spet-to — O-
And you might have more faith in me as well! I trust you with me. Now,
(stepping between them.)
G.
là, finiam le di-spu-te! Se su-bi-to sen-za al-tro re-pli-car non te ne
now... Let's not be quar-rel-some. I would not wish to change for bad my ear-ly good im-
G.
va-i, Ma-set-to, guar-da ben, ti pen-ti-ra-i!
pres-sion: Ma-set-to, be dis-creet; or else—be sor-ry!
(Touching his sword.)

No. 6. "Ho capito."

Aria.

(aside to Zerlina.)
M.
me, a - ver per me, a - ver per me. Bricco-naccia, ma-lan-dri - na, fostio -
word, and keep their word, and keep their word. Hap-py, aren't you? I could kill you! So you'll
cresc.
f
p
(To Leporello who wants to lead him off.)
gnor la mia ru - i - na, fos-ti o - gnor la mia ru - i - na! Ven-go, vengo!
play the strum-pet, will you! So you'll play the strum-pet, will you! Just a mo-ment.
fp
fp
cresc.
f
p
(to Zerlina.)
(aside, bitterly.)
Re-sta, re - sta! E u - na co - sa mol - to o - ne - sta!
For the last time . . . Do not make my love your pas-time.
cresc.
f
Strings.
p
(to Zerlina and Don G.)
(sarcastically to Zerlina.)
Faccia il no-stro Ca - va - lie - re Ca - va - lie - ra an - co - ra te, Ca - va -
When his Lord-ship woos a maid-en She be - comes Mi - la - dy too She be -
Tutti.
f
p
(aside to Zerlina.)
liera an - co - ra te. Bric - co - nac - cia, ma - lan - dri - na! fo - sti o -
comes Mi - la - dy too. No, Zer - li - na . . . I won't let you. How I

M.
gnor la mia ru - i - na, fo - sti o - gnor la mia ru - i - na!
wish I'd nev - er met you! How I wish I'd nev - er met you!
cresc.
f
p
(to Leporello.)
(to Zerlina.)
Ven - go, ven - go! Re - sta, re - sta! è u - na co - sa
Let's be go - ing. So, I'll leave you. Do not let this
cresc.
mol - to o - ne - sta! faccia il no - stro Ca - va - lie - re Ca - va -
part - ing grieve you. When his Lord-ship woos a maid-en She be -
(to Zerlina.)
liera an - co - ra te, Ca - va - liera an - co - ra te, faccia il no - stro Ca - va -
comes Mi - la - dy too, If the fair - y - tales are true. When his Lord-ship woos a
ten.
f p
cresc.

M.
lie - re Ca - va - lie - ra an - co - ra te, faccia il no - stro Ca - va -
maid - en She be - comes Mi - la - dy too. When his Lord - ship woos a
ten.
f
p
cresc.
lie - re Ca - va - lie - ra anco - ra te, Ca - va - lie - ra an - co - ra
maid - en She be - comes Mi - la - dy too. If the fair - y - tales are
te, Ca - va - lie - ra an - co - ra te! (Exit with Leporello, who hurries him into the Tavern.)
true, You'll be - come a la - dy too.
Recit.
Don Giovanni.
G.
Al - fin siam li - be - ra - ti, Zerli - net - ta gen - til, da quel scioc - co - ne, che ne di - te, mio
And we're a - lone, Zer - li - na, for the first time a - lone with - out that id - iot... was it not ver - y
(trying to embrace her.) Zerlina. (drawing back.) Don Giovanni.
G. Z. G.
ben? sò far pu - li - to? Si - gno - re, è mio ma - ri - to! Chi? co - lui? vi par che un o - nest'
neat, how I dis - patched him? But, sir, we're getting mar - ried! You! To him! What can he know of

G.
uo - mo, un no - bil Ca - va - lier, qual io mi van - to, pos - sa sof -
beau-ty? And how can I, who live by fine per - cep - tions, see - ing your
frir che quel vi - set - to d'o - ro, quel vi-so in-zuc-che - ra - to da un bi - fol-cac-cio
grace and sens - ing your re-fine-ment, how can I see you wast-ed in ser - vi - tude to
Zerlina.
vil sia stra - paz - za - to? Ma Si - gnor, io gli die - di pa -
that un - wor - thy bump-kin?! But, my lord, I can hard - ly go
Don Giovanni.
ro - la di spo-sar - lo. Tal pa - ro - la non va - le un ze - ro: voi non
back on my prom-ise! It would hard - ly be right to keep it! Is a
sie - te fat - ta per es - ser pa - e - sa - na, un al - tra sor - te vi pro -
prom-ise sa - cred that would en-slave a god-dess? I dare not think so, when a
cu - ran que - gli oc-chi bric - con-cel - li, quei lab-bret-ti si bel - li, quel - le di - tuc - cia
glance more vi - va - cious than Au - ro - ra, a Di - a - na's complex-ion, lips that the Queen of
can-di-de e o-do - ro - se; par - mi toc-car giun - ca - ta, e fiu - tar ro - se. Ah, non vor -
Love her-self must en-vy, are in them-selves a prom - ise of no - ble for - tune! But I'm a -
Zerlina.
G.
Z.

Don Giovanni.
Zerlina.
Z.
G.
Z.
re - i — Che non vor - re - ste? Al - fi - ne in-gan - na - ta re -
fraid, sir . . . A - fraid of for - tune? Not that, sir . . . I'm a - fraid of de -
Z.
star. Io sò che ra - ro col - le don - ne voi al - tri ca - va - lie - ri sie - te o -
ceit. I hear too of - ten how you no - ble-men treat us coun-try maid-ens when your
Don Giovanni.
Z.
G.
ne - sti e sin-ce - ri. Eh, un im-po - stu - ra del - la gen - te ple - be - a! la no - bil -
prom-is - es win us. Slan - der-ous rav - ings of the en - vi - ous low born! A man of
G.
tà ha di - pin - ta ne - gli oc - chi l'o - ne - stà. Or - sù, non per - diam
birth has an hon - es - ty na - tive to his blood! Be not a - fraid, my
Zerlina.
G.
Z.
tem - po; in que - sto i - stan - te io vi vo - glio spo - sar. Voi?
dear - est; sub - mit to for - tune. We'll be mat - ed to - day! Sir!
Don Giovanni.
(pointing to his castle.)
G.
Cer - to, i - o. Quel ca - si - net - to è mi - o, so - li sa - re - mo. E
Sir, no long - er. Soon, in the book of Heav - en, your name and my name will
G.
là, gio - jel - lo mi - o, ci spo - se - re - mo.
al - ways be to - geth - er— Don - na Zer - li - na!

Nº 7. "Là ci darem la mano."

Duettino.

Zerlina.
G.
Z.
sor — te! Pre - sto non son — più for - te, non son più for - te, non son — più
long - er! Faint - - ly I would that I were strong - er. that I — were — strong - - er. that I — were
Tutti.
p
Cor.
p
(Donna Elvira appears on the verandah of the main building, and watches what is going on.)
Z.
for - te!
strong-er.
Vor -
I
Don Giovanni.
G.
Vie - ni! vie - ni! Là ci da - rem la ma - no,
Dear - est, gent - ly, Here with our hands en - twin - ing.
sfp
Z.
rei, e non vor - re - i, Mi trema un po - co il
fear you may de - ceive me I trem - ble to de -
G.
Là mi di - rai di sì,
Why not walk on with me?
p
Z.
cor; ma — può bur - lar - mi an -
part. Should — I o - bey — my
G.
par - tiam, ben mio, da qui.
Let our de - signs a - gree:

(disengaging
Z.
cor. Mi fa-pie-tà Ma-set-to; pre-
heart? Must poor Ma-set-to suf-fer? Dear-
(putting his arm around her.)
G.
Vie-ni, mio bel di-let-to! io can-gie-rò tua
Come to your no-ble lov-er! Peas-ant you'll be no
mf
p
mf
herself, and escaping to other side.)
Z.
sto non son più for-te, non son piu for-te, non son più for-te!
ly I hope I can be strong-er, I can be strong-er, I can be strong-er.
G.
sor-te. An-
long-er. My
p
(throwing herself into his arms.)
Allegro.
Z.
An-diam! An-diam, an-diam, mio be-ne, a
I will! To-geth-er let us pure-ly In-
(insistently)
G.
diam! An-diam! An-diam, an-diam, mio be-ne, a
love! Be mine! To-geth-er let us pure-ly In-
Allegro.
Z.
ri-sto-rar le pe-ne d'un' in-no-cen-te a-mor!
dulge a whim we sure-ly Are fault-less to ful-fill.
G.
ri-sto-rar le pe-ne d'un' in-no-cen-te a-mor!
dulge a whim we sure-ly Are fault-less to ful-fill.

Z.
An-diam, an-diam, mio be-ne, a ri-sto-rar le pe-ne d'un'
For no-ble-man and peas-ant, While do-ing what is pleas-ant Can-

G.
An-diam, an-diam, mio be-ne, a ri-sto-rar le pe-ne d'un'
For no-ble-man and peas-ant, While do-ing what is pleas-ant Can-

(Donna Elvira descends the steps, and posts herself at centre, back.)

Z.
in-no-cen-te a-mor!
not be do-ing ill.

G.
in-no-cen-te a-mor! An-diam!
not be do-ing ill. Con-sent!

Fl. *p* pizz.

Z.
An-diam! An-diam!
My love! Be true.

G.
An-
I

arco

Z.
An-diam, mio bene, an-diam, le pe-ne a ri-sto-rar d'un
We'll go with-out de-lay, And cheer-ful-ly at play Love

G.
diam! An-diam, mio bene, an-diam, le pe-ne a ri-sto-rar, d'un
will! We'll go with-out de-lay, And cheer-ful-ly at play Love

Z.
in - no - cen-te a - mor!
in - no - cent - ly still.
(Exeunt, arm in arm.)
G.
in - no - cen-te a - mor!
in - no - cent - ly still.
Recit.
Donna Elvira (desperately, intercepting Don Giovanni.)
E.
Fer - ma - ti, scel - le - ra - to! il ciel mi fe - ce u - dir le tue per -
Dare to go one step fur - ther! Thank God I have ar - rived in time to
fi - die; io so - no a tem - po di sal - var que - sta mi - se - ra in - no -
stop you, ex - pose your base - ness, and pre - vent one poor in - no - cent be -
Zerlina.
cen - te dal tuo bar - ba - ro ar - ti - glio! Me - schi - na! co - sa
com - ing one more tear - ful re - pent - ant! What is the la - dy
Don Giovanni. (aside.)
(softly to Elvira.)
sen - to! (Amor, con - si - glio!) I - dol mio, non ve - de - te, ch'io vo - glio di - ver -
say - ing? (That's all I need - ed!) Do be rea - son - able, dear - est I'm look - ing for a -
Donna Elvira (aloud.)
tir - mi? Di - ver - tir - ti? è ve - ro! di - ver - tir - ti! io sò, cru -
muse - ment. For a - muse - ment! Pre - cise - ly! For a - muse - ment! A - las I

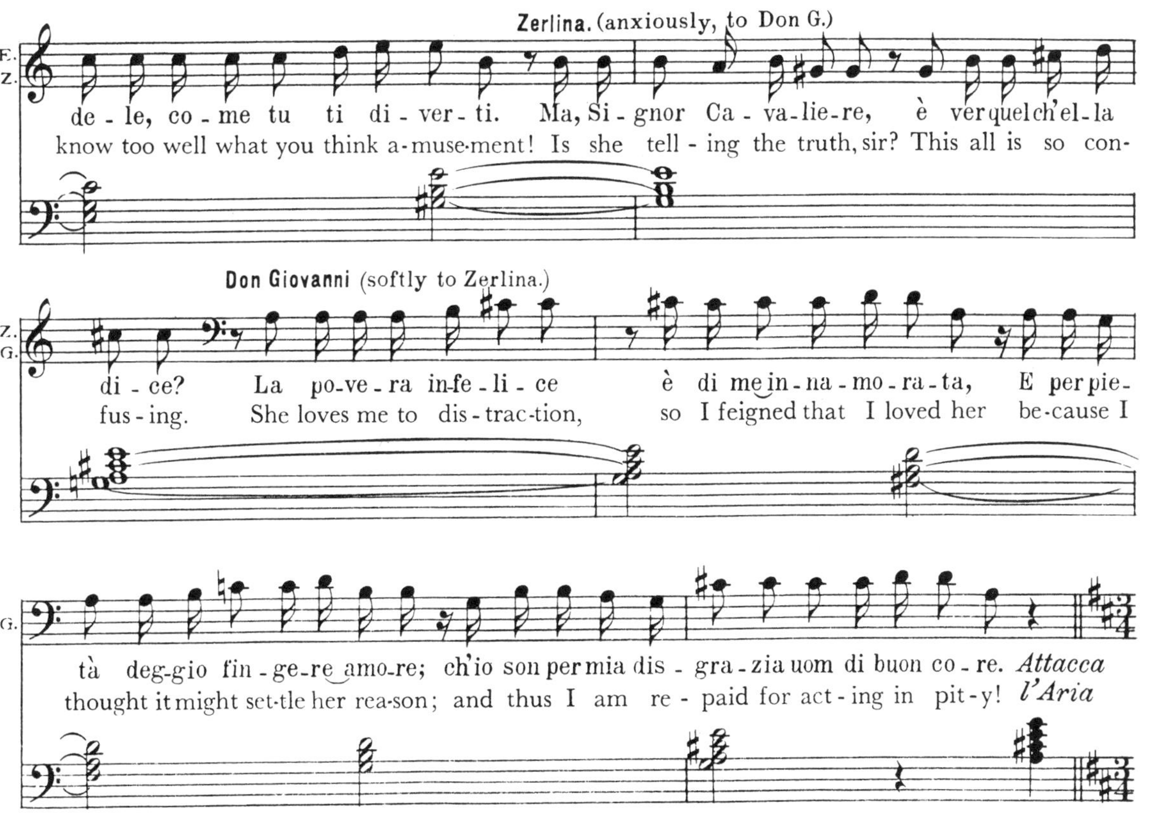

Nº 8. "Ah! fuggi il traditor!„
Aria.

E.
tor, fal-la - - - ce il ci - - glio!
lie And false his beam-ing eye.
f
Da miei tor-men-ti im-pa-ra a
Too well, too long I lis-tened, Too
p
cre-der a quel cor; e na - - sca il tuo ti-mor dal mio
well he played his part, Too late I know him now: Be-lieve
pe-ri - - glio, ah fug-gi, fug - - gi! ah
a brok-en heart. O hear me, hear me, O
fug-gi il tra-di-tor! non lo la-sciar più dir; il
hear me, I im-plore! Pay heed to him no more. His

E.
labbro è men - ti - tor, fal-la - ce il ci - glio, il
words are all a lie And false his beam-ing eye. His
lab - bro è men - ti - tor, fal - la -
words are all a lie And false
ce il ci - glio, sì, fal - la -
his beam-ing eye. Ah! How false
(Exit, leading off Zerlina.)
ce il ci - glio!
that beam-ing eye!
f
Recit. Don Giovanni.
(Enter Donna Anna and D. Octavio, dressed in mourning.)
G.
Mi par ch'oggi il de-mo-nio si di - ver - ta d'op-por-si a' miei pia - ce - vo - li pro -
To hell with this ex - as - per - at - ing morn-ing! The ver - y dev - il seems to be a -

Don Octavio.
G.
O.
gres - si; van-no mal tut - ti quan-ti. Ah ch'o-ra i - do - lo mio, son va-ni i
gainst me! Noth-ing goes as I planned it. I'm cer-tain he will help. He has great
O.
(perceiving Don G.)
pian - ti, di ven-det - ta si par - li! Oh Don Gio - van - ni!
in-fluence. He is brave and re - source-ful. Come, let us ask him!
Don Giovanni. (aside.)
Donna Anna. (to D. Giovanni.)
G.
A.
(Man - ca - va questo in ver!) Si - gno - re, a tem - po vi ri - tro -
(And now the fi - nal straw!) God save you who sent you just at this
A.
G.
Don Giovanni.
viam: a - ve - te co - re? a - ve - te a - ni - ma ge - ne - ro - sa? (Sta a ve -
time! I have been hear-ing a - bout your gen - er - ous kind - ly na - ture. (I shall
(aside.)
(aloud, to D. Anna.)
G.
de - re che il dia - vo - lo le ha det - to qual-che co - sa.) Che do - man - da! per - chè?
not be sur-prised to hear the dev - il has been talk-ing!) I am flat-tered. But why?
Donna Anna.
Don Giovanni. (aside.)
A.
G.
Bi - so-gno abbia - mo del - la vo - stra ami - ci - zia. (Mi torna il fia - to in
Nev - er did an - y have more need of your friend-ship! (My luck is with me
(aloud)
G.
cor - po.) Co - man - da - te; i con - giun - ti, i pa - ren - ti, que - sta
this time!) I am hon - ored! All my house-hold, all my kin - dred, all my
(With much warmth.)
G.
man, que - sto fer - ro, i be - ni, il san - gue spen - de - rò per ser -
goods, my in - ven - tion, my cun - ning, my life it - self are all at your

G.
vir - vi: ma voi, bel - la Donn' An - na, per - chè co - sì pian -
serv - ice. But what, gra - cious young la - dy, has caused that look of
G.
ge - te? il cru - de - le chi fù che o - sò la cal - ma tur - bar del vi - ver
sor - row? It were bet - ter to die than dare to in - jure so pure, so fair a
Donna Elvira (entering).
G.
E.
vo - stro? Ah, ti ri - tro - vo an - cor, per - fi - do mo - stro?
crea - ture! Ah, at your lies a - gain! I shall ex - pose you!
Nº 9. "Non ti fidar, o misera."
Andante.
Quartet.
Donna Elvira. (to D. Anna.)
Voice.
E.
Non ti fi - dar, o mi - se - ra, di quel ri - bal - do cor!
No - ble and kind he seems to be, I once be - lieved him true:
Piano.
Strings.
E.
me già tra - dì quel bar - ba - ro, te vuol tra - dir an - cor.
Know that this man was false to me, And will be false to you.
p cresc.
mf
p
Vln.
Donna Anna. (aside, withdrawing a little.)
A.
Cie - li! che aspetto no - bi - le! che dol - ce ma - es - tà! Il
Weep - ing? Sel - dom have I be - held Such grace and maj - es - ty. What
Don Octavio.
O.
Cie - li! che aspetto no - bi - le! che dol - ce ma - es - tà! Il
Weep - ing? Sel - dom have I be - held Such grace and maj - es - ty. What
Cl.
Fl.

(Don G. tries to persuade Donna Elvira to step aside, but she refuses; finally he grasps her right hand, and draws her away toward his right.)
A.
suo do-lor, le la-gri-me m'empiono di pie-tà, m'em-piono di pie-
makes her look so sor-row-ful, What can her sto-ry be? What can her sto-ry
O.
suo do-lor, le la-gri-me m'empiono di pie-tà, m'em-piono di pie-
makes her look so sor-row-ful, What can her sto-ry be? What can her sto-ry
cresc.
mf
p
Cl.
Fl.
A.
tà!
be?
Don Giovanni (whispers, D. Elvira listens.)
O.
G.
tà! La po-ve-ra ra-gaz-za è pazza, a-mi-ci mie-i! lascia-te-mi con
be? She's men-tal-ly af-flict-ed And weeps when con-tra-dict-ed: Stand back or you'll up-
cresc.
G.
le-i, è paz-za, a-mi-ci mie-i, for-se si cal-me-rà, for-
set her. I know these cas-es bet-ter. Leave her a-lone with me, Leave
f
p cresc.
mf
p
Donna Elvira.
E.
Ah! non cre-de-te al per-fi-do!
He lies: he is de-ceiv-ing you!
G.
-se si cal-me-rà! È paz-za, non ba-
her a-lone with me. Poor girl, you must ex-
Fl.
Cl.

Donna Anna. (aside.)
A.
A chi si cre-de-rà? a chi si cre-de-
Whom ought we to be-lieve? Whom ought we to be-
E.
Re-sta - te, oh Dei - re - sta - te!
O God! You must be - lieve - me!
Don Octavio. (aside.)
O.
A chi si cre-de-rà? a chi si cre-de-
Whom ought we to be-lieve? Whom ought we to be-
G.
da - te!
cuse her!
è pazza!
She's cra-zy!
rà? a chi si cre-de-rà? si cre - de - rà?
lieve? Which one should we be-lieve, Whose word be - lieve?
Re-sta-te!
Be-lieve me!
Ah non cre-de-te al per - fi - do! re -
He lies, he is de - ceiv - ing you, be -
rà? a chi si cre-de-rà? si cre - de - rà?
lieve? Which one should we be-lieve, Whose word be - lieve?
tr
tr

A.
Cer - to mo - to d'i - gno - to tor - men - to
Some-thing tells me there's more to dis - cov - er,
F.
sta - te! Sde - gno, rabbia, di - spet - to, spa -
lieve me! Scorn and an - ger and ha-tred as -
C.
Cer - to mo - to d'i - gno - to tor - men - to
Some-thing tells me there's more to dis - cov - er,
(aside)
G.
Cer - to mo - to d'i - gno - to tor - men - to
Will they guess that there's more to dis - cov - er?
Fl.
Vlns.
cresc.
f
p
A.
Den-tro l'al - ma gi - ra - re mi sen - to,
I be - gin to be filled with sus - pi - cion,
F.
ven - to den - tro l'al - ma gi - ra - re mi
sist me! Give me cour-age to make my de -
C.
Den-tro l'al - ma gi - ra - re mi sen - to,
I be - gin to be filled with sus - pi - cion,
G.
Den-tro l'al - ma gi - ra - re mi sen - to,
I can see they are filled with sus - pi - cion.
cresc.
f
p

che mi di - ce per quel - la in - fe - li - ce
I be - lieve this poor la - dy could tell us
sen - to, Che mi di - ce di quel tra - di -
ci - sion! Let him trem - ble! I'm go - ing to
Che mi di - ce per
I be - lieve this poor
Che mi di - ce per quel - la in - fe -
In her fol - ly I fear she will
Vln.
Cor.
Viol
cen - to co - se, che in - ten - der, che inten - der non sa, no,
Man - y things, (dread - ful things), that we dare not sus - pect. What,
to - re cen - to co - se, che inten - der non sa, no, Che mi
tell them All the things that they do not sus - pect. Let him
quel - la in - fe - li - ce cen - to co - se, che in - ten - der non sa, no.
la - dy could tell us Man - y things, that we dare not sus - pect. What,
li - ce cen - to co - se, che inten - der non sa, no,
tell them What I hoped they would nev - er sus - pect. What,

A.
no! che in - ten - der non
what we dare not sus-
E.
di-ce di quel tra-di-to - re, di quel tra-di - to - re cen-to co - se, che intender non
tremble! I am go-ing to tell them All the things that they do not sus-
O.
p
no! che in - ten - der non
what we dare not sus-
G.
p
no! cen - to co - se, che inten - der non
what what I hoped they would nev - er sus-
p
A.
sa, che in - ten - der non sa!
pect, we dare not sus-pect.
E.
sa, che mi di - ce, mi di - ce di quel tra-di-to - re, cen-to co - se che intender non sa!
pect. Let him tremble! I'm go-ing to tell them All the things that they do not sus-pect.
O.
sa, che in - ten - der non sa!
pect, we dare not sus-pect.
G.
sa, cen - to co - se che inten - der non sa!
pect, What I hoped they would nev - er sus-pect.
Vln.
Cl.
Fag.

Don Octavio (aside.)
O.
Io di quà non va-do vi-a, se non so com' è l'af-far!
I shall stay till I dis-cov-er who is ly-ing, he or she.
Donna Anna (aside.)
A.
Non ha l'a-ria di paz-zi-a il suo tratto, il suo par-lar.
There is noth-ing mad a-bout her words or looks that I can see.
Don Giovanni.
G.
Se men
They sus-
va-do, si po-tri-a qual-che co-sa so-spet-tar.
pect me. If I go now, they will think that I'm a-fraid.
Donna Elvira. (to
E.
Da quel
His the
Don G., in exasperation.)
Don Octavio (to D. Giov.)
E.
O.
cef-fo si do-vri-a la ner' al-ma giu-di-car. Dunque quella?
ly-ing, his the cun-ning, mine the in-no-cence be-trayed! What do you say?
È paz-za-
She's mad, I

Donna Anna (to Donna Elvira.)
Dun-que que-gli?
What do you say?
Donna Elvira.
(to Don G.)
È un tra - di - to - re, men - ti -
That he be-trayed me. You be -
Don Giovanni.
(tries to seperate D. Anna and Elvira.)
rel-la! In - fe - li - ce!
tell you. Pure de - lu - sion!
sf
In - co -
She has
Don Octavio.
to - re, men - ti - to - re, men - ti - to - re! In - co -
trayed me! You be-trayed me! You be - trayed me! She has
f
Vlns.
p
min - cio a du - bi - tar.
been be-trayed, I fear.
min - cio a du - bi - tar.
been be-trayed, I fear.
(softly to Donna Elvira.)
Zit - ta, zit - ta, che la gen - te si ra - duna a noi d'in-
Stop it, stop it, stop this mo-ment, Do not make a scene in
Fl. & Strings.
pp

G.
tor - no. Sia-te un po - co più pru - den - te, vi fa - re - te cri - ti -
pub - lic. Do con - trol your - self, I beg you. Have you lost all sense of
Donna Elvira (to Don Giovanni.)
E.
Non sperarlo, o scel - le - ra - to, ho per - du - ta la pruden - za,
Vil-lain, you shall nev-er stop me. Nei-ther fear nor shame can stop me.
G.
car.
shame?
f
p
E.
le tue colpe ed il mio sta - to voglio a tut-ti pa - le - sar, vo-glio a
But the wrong that you have done me, To the world I shall pro-claim, To the
Donna Anna (aside, observing Don Giovanni.)
A.
Que - gli ac-cen - ti sì som-
Mark his man - ner. How it
E.
tut-ti pa - le-sar! Non sperarlo, o scel - le - ra - to!
world I shall pro-claim. Vil-lain, you shall nev-er stop me.
(aside)
Don Octavio.
O.
Que - gli ac-cen - ti sì som-
Mark his man - ner. How it
Don Giovanni.
G.
Zit - ta, zit - ta, che la gen-te si ra-du-na a noi d'in-
Stop it, stop it, stop this mo-ment, Do not make a scene in
Vlns.
fp

A.
mes - - si, quel can -
chang - - es. How he
E.
ho per - du - ta la pru - den - za!
Nei - ther fear nor shame can stop me.
O.
mes - - si, quel can -
chang - - es. How he
G.
tor - no, siate un po - co più pru -
pub - lic. Do con - trol your - self, I
cresc.
giar - - - - - si di co - lo - re, son in-
frowns and how he whis-pers. I be-
le tue col-pe ed il mio sta - to vo - glio a tut - ti pa - le -
But the wrong that you have done me, To the world I shall pro -
giar - - - - - si di co - lo - re, son in-
frowns and how he whis-pers. I be-
den - te, vi fa - re - te cri - ti - car,
beg you. Have you lost all sense of shame?
Clar.

A.
di - zi trop - po e - spres - si, che mi
gin to doubt his sto - ry. Can it
E.
sar, ho per - du - ta la pru - den - za!
claim. Nei - ther fear nor shame can stop me.
O.
di - zi trop - po e - spres - si, che mi
gin to doubt his sto - ry. Can it
G.
sia - te un po - co più pru - den - te!
Do con - trol your - self, I beg you.
A.
fan de - ter - mi - nar, che mi
be that he's to blame? Can it
E.
Non spe - rar - lo! ho per - du - ta la pru-
Try to stop me. Nei-ther fear nor shame can
O.
fan de - ter - mi - nar, che mi
be that he's to blame? Can it
G.
zit - to, zit - to! si ra - du - na a noi d'in - tor - no!
Stop it, stop it, Do not make a scene in pub - lic.
Vln.

A.
E.
O.
G.
fan de - ter - mi - nar, che mi
be that he's to blame? Can it
den-za,' non sperarlo, o scelle-ra - to! le tue colpe, ed il mio
stop me. Vil-lain, you shall nev-er stop me. But the wrong that you have
fan de - ter - mi - nar, che mi
be that he's to blame? Can it
zit-to, zit - to! che la gen-te siate un poco più pruden - te!
Stop it, stop it, stop this mo-ment, Do con-trol your-self, I beg you.
fan de - ter - mi - nar!
be that he's to blame?
sta - to vo - glio a tut - ti pa - le - sar!
done me, To the world I shall pro-claim.
fan de - ter - mi - nar!
be that he's to blame?
(Don G. mastering Donna Elvira by his gaze, leads her away, and then returns.)
vi fa-re-te, vi fa - re - te cri - ti - car!
Have you lost all sense of shame, all sense of shame?
Fl.
Cl.
pp

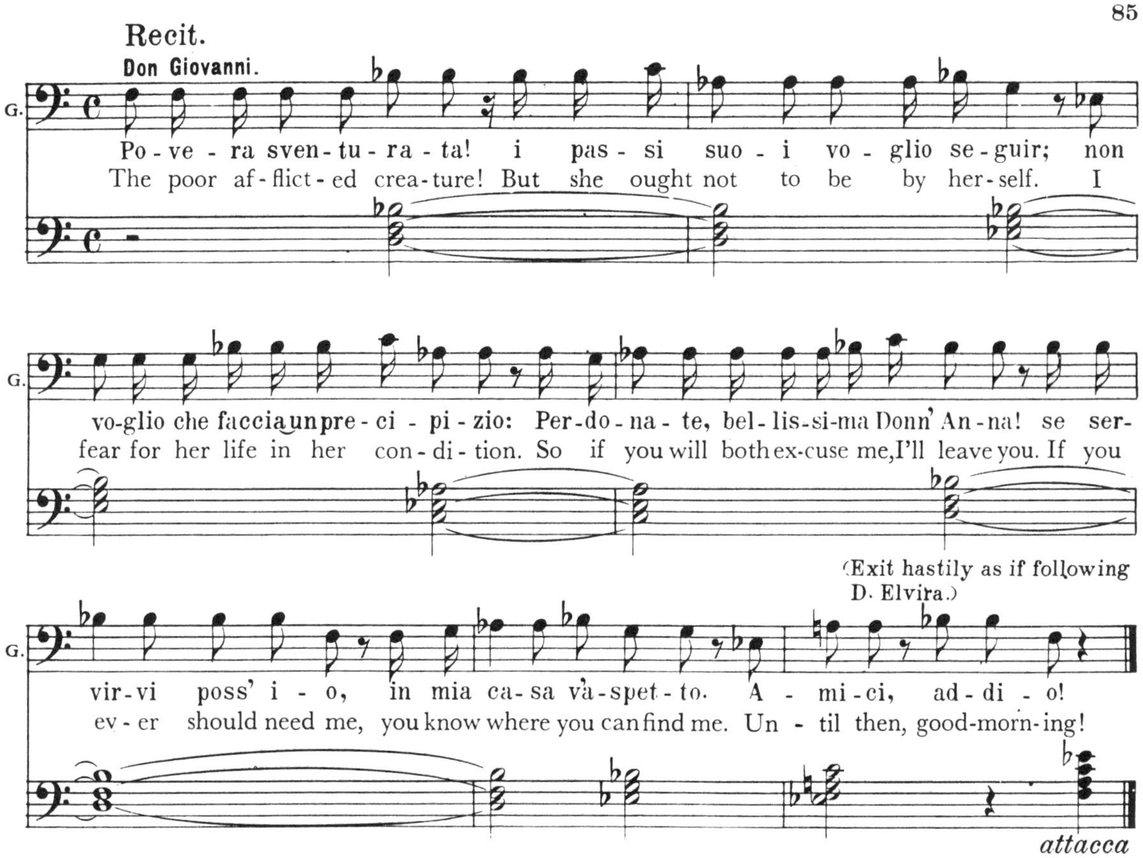

Recit.

Don Giovanni.

G.

Po - ve - ra sven - tu - ra - ta! i pas - si suo - i vo - glio se - guir; non
The poor af - flict - ed crea - ture! But she ought not to be by her - self. I

G.

vo - glio che faccia un pre - ci - pi - zio: Per - do - na - te, bel - lis - si - ma Donn' An - na! se ser -
fear for her life in her con - di - tion. So if you will both ex - cuse me, I'll leave you. If you

(Exit hastily as if following D. Elvira.)

G.

vir - vi poss' i - o, in mia ca - sa v'a - spet - to. A - mi - ci, ad - di - o!
ev - er should need me, you know where you can find me. Un - til then, good-morn - ing!

attacca

Nº 10.a "Don Ottavio! son morta!,,

Recitative.

Don Octavio.
Donna Anna.
re - te-mi! Mio be - ne, fa - te co - rag-gio! O De - i!
come to me! My dear-est, what is the mat-ter? I know now!
(Pointing after Don G., with uplifted arm.)
O De - i! Quegli è il car-
I know now! That was the
Don Octavio.
Donna Anna.
ne - fi - ce del pa - dre mi - o! Che di - te? Non du - bi - ta - te
mur - der - er! He killed my fath - er! You're cer - tain? Cer - tain be - yond all
più; gli ul - ti - mi ac - cen - ti che l'em - pio pro - fe - rì, tut - ta la
doubt! His ev - 'ry ges - ture, his words be - fore he left, Each in - to -
p
Basso only
D. Octavio.
vo - ce, ri - chia - mar nel cor mio di quell' in - deg - no, che nel mio apparta - mento Oh
na - tion, brought to mind all at once With star - tling clear - ness, the lib - er - tine in - trud - er... O
ciel! pos - si - bi - le, che sot - to il sa - cre man - to d'a - mi - ci - zia ma co - me
no! I can't be - lieve that he would dare To of - fer his as - sist - ance But tell me

Donna Anna. (quieter, repressing her emotions).
O.
A.
fù, nar-ra-te-mi lo strano av-ve-ni-men-to.
all, all that un-til to-day your grief had hid-den.
E - ra già al-quanta a-van-
Mid-night had sounded. All the
Str.
f Andante.
p
za-ta la not-te, quando nel-le mie stan-ze, o-ve so-let-ta mi trovai per sven-
cit-y was qui-et. I dis-missed my du-en-na; and Near my bed, at my de-vo-tions was
tu-ra, en-trar io vi- - - di in un man-tello av-vol-to un uom che al primo i-
kneel-ing, When there ap-peared a man, his cloak A-bout him I thought him you a
stan-te a-vea pre-so per voi; ma ri-co-nob-bi poi, che un' in-
mo-ment And I gent-ly re-proached him; but then I saw How dread-ful-ly
Don Octavio. (agitated)
Donna Anna.
gan-no e-ra il mi-o! Stel-le! se-gui-te! Ta-ci-to a me sap-
I was mis-tak-en. Quick-ly! Con-tin-ue! Si-lent-ly he ap-
p Andante.
pres-sa, e mi vuo-le ab-brac-ciar; scio-glier-mi cer-co, ei più mi
proached me. I was dragged to my feet, pulled to him rough-ly. He tried to
stringendo il tempo
cresc.

A.
strin - ge _ io gri - do!
kiss me. I shout-ed,
non vie-ne al -
but No one
Tempo I.
Tutti
cun; con u - na ma - no cer - ca d'im - pe - di - re la vo - ce,
heard. With one hand I was sti - fled To pre - vent me from scream-ing;
Str.
p Andante.
e coll' al - tra m'af - fer - ra stret - ta co - sì, che già mi cre - do
with the oth - er He pressed me ev - er more close. I thought That he must
Don Octavio (in extreme agitation)
Donna Anna.
O.
vin - ta. Per - fi - do! e al - fin? Al - fi - ne il duol, l'or - ro - re dell' in - fa - me at - ten -
con - quer! Hor - ri - ble! And then? And then my will, in shock re - born, With ter - ror in -
ta - to ac - creb - be sì la le - na mi - a, che a for - za di svin - co -
hu - man, re - stored my dwin - dled For - ces doub - ly, and I could re - new My
fp
lar - mi, tor - cer - mi e pie - gar - mi da lui mi sciol - si!
strug - gle, strike at him, and with fu - ry tear My - self from him!
Don Octavio.
Ohi - mè! re -
Then God had

Donna Anna.
O.
A.
spi - ro. Al - lo - ra rin - for - zo i stri - di mie - i,
heard you! When once I was free, I screamed more loud - ly.
chia - mo soc -
"Help me!" I
f Tempo I.
cor - so,
shout - ed.
fug - ge il fel - lon,
He fled in fear;
ar -
But
di - ta - men - te il se - guo fin nel - la stra - da per fer - mar - lo, e
I more quick - ly fol - lowed in - to The street it - self to stop him, To
so - no as - sa - li - tri - ce d'as - sa - li - ta;
see him, and the pur - sued be - came the pur - suer.
Il pa - dre vac -
My fath - er came
cor - re, vuol co - no - scer - lo, e l'in - de - gno, che del po - ve - ro
run - ning. I was des - per - ate, and I left them To a - rouse all the
vec - chio e - ra più for - te, com - piè il mi - sfat - to su - o,
aid I might for my fath - er, There to de - fend my hon - or.

(in an agony of grief, almost collapsing.)
com - pie il mi - sfat - to su - o, col dar - gli mor - te.
Yet, An old man de - fense - less, there he was mur - dered!
"Or sai, chi l'onore.,,
Aria.
Andante.
Donna Anna. (collecting herself, with lofty energy.)
Voice.
Piano.
Strings.
p
Or sai, chi l'o - no - re ra - pi - re a me vol - se, che fù il tra - di - to - re, che il padre, che il pa - dre mi tol - se. Vendet - ta ti chieg - go, la
You know who is guilt - y, The lech - er as - sas - sin Who dared my dis - honor And struck down, and struck down my fath - er! The shade of my fath - er, For
Ob.
Fag.
Corni sustain.

A.
chie - de il tuo cor, la
venge - ance it cries, For
chie - de il tuo cor. Ram - men - ta la
venge - ance it cries! If but for a
pia - ga del mi - se - ro se - no, ri -
mo - ment You fal - ter in pur - pose, In -
mi - ra di san - gue co - per - to, co - per - to il ter -
voke, then, his bod - y, His blood on the stones in the
re - no, se l'i - rain te lan - gue d'un giu - sto fu - ror,
torch-light, And, fresh in that vis - ion, Your fu - ry will rise,
Ob.
Vlns.
Fag.
Bassi.
Tutti.
f

largamente
A.
d'un giu - sto fu - ror! Or sai chi l'o -
Your fu - ry will rise. Your love and your
p
Bassi
no - re ra - pi - re a me vol - se, chi
hon - or Must nour - ish your ha - tred In
Ob. Fag.
fù il tra - di - to - re, che il pa - dre, che il pa - dre mi
one ded - i - ca - tion To strike down, to strike down the
tol - se, ven - det - ta ti chieg - go, la
kill - er, Your life have one vis - ion, To
chie - de il tuo cor, la
see that he dies, To
chie - de il tuo cor! Ram - men - ta la pia - ga, ri -
see that he dies! My fath - er, I see him! He
f

A.
mi-ra di san-gue! Ven-det - ta ti chieg - go, la
wan-ders, un-shriv-en, Be - tween earth and heav - en, For
p f p p
A.
chie - de il tuo cor, la
venge - ance he cries, For
A.
chie - de il tuo cor, ven-det - ta ti chieg - go, la chie - de il tuo
venge - ance he cries. Re - armed in that vis - ion, Your fu - ry will
Winds sustain
f p
A.
cor, ven-det - ta ti chieg - go, la chie - de il tuo cor, la chie - de il
rise, To search out the kill - er, To see that he dies, To see that
f p sf p
A.
tuo - cor, la chie - de il tuo - cor, la chie - de il tuo
he dies, To see that he dies! The hor - ri - ble
sf p

A. cor, la chie - de il tuo cor; ven - det - ta ti chieg-go, la
scene Is clear to my eyes: The blood of my fath-er, For

cresc.

A. chie - de il tuo cor!
venge - ance it — cries! (Exit.)

f *p*

Recit.

Don Octavio. (alone.)

O. Co - me mai cre - der deg - gio, di sì ne - ro de - lit - to ca -
Can it be that a per - son of such high birth is guilt - y of

O. pa - ce un ca - va - lie - re! Ah, di - sco - pri - re il ve - ro o - gni
an. a - tro - cious mur - der? Loth am I still to think it. But my

O. mez - zo si cer - chi; io sen - to in pet - to e di spo - so e d'a -
prom - ise has bound me. And now the voic - es of af - fec - tion and of

O. mi - co il do - ver che mi par - la; Dis - in - gan - nar la vo - glio, o ven - di - car - la!
du - ty speak in cho - rus to - geth - er: "Prove that she was mis - tak - en, or else a - venge her!"

No. 10b "Dalla sua pace."

Aria.

O.
be-ne, s'el-la non l'ha, e non ho be-ne, s'el-la non l'ha!
prais-es Where-'er you go. O sing_ her_ prais-es Where-'er you go.
Wind
cresc.
f
Dal-la sua pa-ce la mia di-pen-de, quel ch'a lei pia-ce,
Shine, lights of heav-en, Guard-ians im-mor-tal, Shine on my true_love,
Str
p
vi-ta mi ren-de, quel che le in-cre-sce, mor-te mi dà, mor-te,
Wak-ing or_sleep-ing; Sun, moon and star-light, Com-fort her woe, Com-fort,
cresc.
mf
f
Cor.
Str
p
cresc.
mor-te mi dà; dal-la sua pa-ce la mia di-pen-de, quel che a lei
Com-fort her woe. While grief be-clouds her I walk in shad-ow, My thoughts are
p
Ob. Fag.
pia-ce, vi-ta mi ren-de,_ quel che le in-cre-sce, mor-te mi dà,
with her, Wak-ing or sleep-ing:_ Sun, moon and star-light, Com-fort our woe,
Fl.
Wind
mf
f

O.
mor - - te, mor - te mi dà, mor - te mi dà, quel che le in-
Com - - fort, Com - fort our woe, Com-fort our woe, Sun, moon and
p
Cor.
cre - sce, morte mi dà!
star - light, Com-fort our woe.
(Exit.)
Tutti.
cresc.
f
tr
Recit.
Leporello (enters from the tavern; after him Don Giovanni, from his villa.)
L.
Io deggio ad o-gni pat-to per sempre abbandonar questo bel mat-to! ec - co - lo quì;
I'm go-ing, got to leave him and soon, be-fore I learn shock-ing bad hab-its. Ah, look at him now,
L.
G.
Don Giovanni. (gaily)
guarda - te, con qual in-dif-fe-ren-za se ne vie-ne! Oh, Le-po-rel-lo mi-o! va tutto
the ras-cal As gay as though he'd noth-ing on his conscience. Hail, uppermost of servants! Are they be-
Leporello. (crossly)
Don Giovanni.
Leporello.
bene? Don Gio-van-ni-no mi-o, va tut - to male! Co - me va tut-to ma-le? Vado a
hav-ing? Hail, neth-er - most of mas-ters! Be-hav-ing bad-ly. What do you mean by bad-ly? As you
Don Giovanni.
ca - sa, co-me m'or-di - na - ste, con tut - ta quel-la gen - te. Bra - vo!
told me I led on those peas-ants got them here inside the cas - tle Bra - vo!

Leporello.
L.
A for-za di chiacche-re, di vez-zi e di bu-gie, ch'ho im-pa-
And there, with much flat-ter-y, ca-jol-er-y and ly-ing all the
L.
G.
Don Giovanni.
ra-to si be-ne a star con vo-i, cer-co d'in-trat-te-ner-li. Bra-vo!
arts I have learned so well from you, sir— did what I could to a-muse them. Bra-vo!
Leporello.
L.
Di-co mil-le co-se a Ma-set-to per pla-car-lo, per trar-gli dal pen-
At the start Ma-set-to ap-peared ex-treme-ly jeal-ous... I man-aged, though, I
L.
G.
L.
Don Giovanni.
Leporello.
sier la ge-lo-si-a— Bra-vo! in co-scien-za mi-a! Fac-cio che
think, to re-as-sure him. Bra-vo! Poor love-sick Ma-set-to! Wine was so
L.
be-va-no, e gli uo-mi-ni e le don-ne son già mez-zi ub-bri-ac-chi:
plen-ti-ful that both the men and wom-en were soon more than half tip-sy.
L.
al-tri can-ta, al-tri scher-za, al-tri se-gui-ta a ber; in sul più
Some were sing-ing, some guf-faw-ing, oth-ers oaf-ish-ly drunk. Then, with-out
L.
G.
L.
Don Giovanni.
(indifferently)
Leporello.
bel-lo chi cre-de-te che ca-pi-ti? Zer-li-na! Bra-vo!
warn-ing... Can you guess who burst in on us? Zer-li-na. Bra-vo!
Don Giovanni. (as before.)
Leporello. (astonished.)
L.
G.
L.
e con lei chi vie-ne? Donna El-vi-ra! Bra-vo! e dis-se di
But guess who was with her! Donn' El-vi-ra. Bra-vo! She talked a-bout

Don Giovanni. (humorously)
Leporello.
voi– Tutto 'quel mal che in boc-ca le ve-ni-a! Bra-vo, in co-sci-en-za
you. Not, I'm a-fraid, in terms of great af-fec-tion. Bra-vo! Poor love-sick Donn'El-
Don Giovanni.
Leporello.
Don Giovanni.
Leporello.
D. Giov.
mi-a! E tu, co-sa fa-ce-sti? Tacqui. Ed el-la? Seguì a gri-dar. E
vi-ra! And what, what did you an-swer? Noth-ing. And she, then... Start-ed scream-ing. And
Leporello.
tu? Quan-do mi par-ve che già fos-se sfo-ga-ta, dol-ce-men-te fuor del-
you... Wait-ed a-while un-til her lungs were ex-haust-ed. Then I gent-ly coaxed her
l'or-to la tras-si, e con bell' ar-te, chiu-sa la por-ta a chia-ve a mi sot-
out through the gar-den. We reached the gate and, while she was talk-ing, I turned the key be-
Don Giovanni.
tra-i, e sul-la via so-let-ta la la-scia-i. Bra-vo!
hind her and left her to her lov-ing med-i-ta-tions. Bra-vo,
bra-vo! ar-ci-bra-vo! l'af-far non può andar me-glio; in-co-min-
bra-vo! Neat-ly man-aged! You could-n't have done bet-ter. The work you've
cia-sti, io sa-prò ter-mi-nar. Trop-po mi pre-mo-no
start-ed shall be mine to com-plete. What a de-light you are,
que-ste con-ta-di-not-te; le vo-glio di-ver-tir finchè vien not-te.
nymphs of pas-ture and mead-ow! I love you one and all. Come to your shep-herd!

Nº 11. "Finch' han dal vino."

Aria.

G.
or-di-ne la danza si-a, chi'l menu-et-to, chi la fo-li-a,
vi-o-lin, Danc-ers go fly-ing, Mad with ex-cite-ment, Puls-es a-throb-bing,

f p *f* Ob. Fag. Fl. *p* *f p*

G.
chi l'a-le-ma-na fa-rai bal-lar, chi'l — menu-et-to fa-rai bal-
Swirl-ing and twirl-ing, Light on the toe. Mad — with ex-cite-ment, Light on the

f p *f p* Ob. Cl. Fag. Vln.

G.
lar, chi — la fol-li-a fa-rai bal-lar, chi — l'a-le-ma-na
toe. Puls-es a-throb-bing, Light on the toe. Swirl-ing and twirl-ing,

G.
fa-rai bal-lar! Ed io frat-tan-to dall' altro can-to con questa e quella
Light on the toe. No-ticed by no-one, I shall be bus-y Play-ing that game where

Ob. Cl. & Cor. sustain. tr tr

G.
vo'a-moreggiar, vo'a-mo-reg-giar, vo'a-mo-reg-giar; — Ah, la mia
Maids cry — O, where maids cry O, Fair maids cry O. — Ah, in the

G.
li - sta do-man mat - ti - na du - na de - ci - na de - vi aumentar,
morn-ing Bring me my list and Down a full doz - en More shall go.
Ah, la mia li - sta d'u - na de - ci - na de - vi aumen-
Yes, in the morn-ing At least a doz - en More shall
tar. Se trovi in piazza qual - che ra - gaz - za, te-co ancor quel - la cer - ca me -
go. Quick, Le - po - rel - lo, Off to the vil - lage, Bring me more girls back, Will-ing or
Tutti.
nar.
no.
Ah la mia li - sta do - man mat - ti - na
Then in the morn-ing Bring me my list and
Fl. Vln.
Fl. & Str.
d'u - na de - ci - na de - vi aumen - tar! Sen - za al - cun or - di - ne,
Down a full doz - en More shall go. While to the vi - o - lin,
Tutti

G.
la danza si - a, chi'l menu - et - to, chi la fol - li - a, chi l'a - le - ma - na
Let them go fly-ing, Mad with ex-cite-ment, Puls - es a-throb-bing, Swirl-ing and twirl-ing,
fp
fa - rai bal - lar. Ah, la mia li - sta do - man mat - ti - na
Light on the toe. Ah, in the morn-ing Bring me my list and
Fl.
Vln.
Ob.
Cl.
Fag.
p
d'u - na de - ci - na de - vi aumen - tar, d'u - na de - ci - na de - vi aumen -
Down a full doz - en More shall go, More than a doz - en Down shall
tr
f
tar, d'u - na de - ci - na de - vi aumen tar, de - vi aumen - tar,
go, More than a doz - en Down shall go, Down they go,
(signs to Leporello to
de - vi aumen - tar, de - vi, de - vi au - men - tar!
Down they go, More, more, more shall go.
cresc.

 fetch the peasants from the tavern; he then hastens into his villa, Leporello going to the tavern.)

M.
uom: ab-bando - nar - mi il di del-le mie noz-ze! porre in fron-te a un vil-la-no d'o -
man, de-sert-ing me the ver-y day of our wed-ding. I'm a ver - y re-spect-a-ble
M.
no-re que-sta mar - ca d'in - famia! Ah, se non fos - se, se non fos-se lo scanda - lo,
fel-low and I won't be dis - hon-ored. Oh if it would-n't, if it would-n't be scan-dal-ous
(goes exitedly to other side.)
Zerlina. (interrupting him)
M.
Z.
vor - re - i – Ma se col - pa io non ho, ma se da lui in - gan-na-ta ri -
I'd give you... It was not what you think! I was sur-prised at a no-ble-man's
Z.
ma - si, e poi che te - mi? tran - quil - la - ti, mia vi - ta: non mi toc -
int' rest, I'd nev - er met one. My won-der made me lin - ger. He nev-er
Z.
cò la pun - ta del - le di - ta: non me lo cre - di? In - gra - to! vien
touched the tip of one small fin - ger! Don't you be - lieve me? All right, then... I'm
(agitatedly)
Z.
qui: sfo - ga - ti, a - maz - za - mi, Fa tut - to di me quelche ti
wrong. Pun - ish me! Be hor - ri - ble! I know and re - pent what I com -
(tenderly)
Z.
pia - ce; Ma poi, Ma - set - to mi - o, ma poi fa pa - ce.
mit - ted — a pure, pa - thet - ic fol - ly — be that ad - mit - ted.
attacca l'aria

Nº 12. "Batti, batti, o bel Masetto."

Aria.

Z.

Lasciе-rò cavar-mi gli occhi, e — le ca - re tue ma -
Strike her down in right-eous fu-ry: She will — then, — so meek-ly —

tr

Z.

ni - ne lie - ta poi sa-prò ba - ciar, sa - prò — ba -
grate - ful, Kiss your — strict - ly lov - ing — hand, O I shall kiss your

f p

Z.

ciar, ba - ciar, sa - prò, — sa - prò ba -
hand, your hand, O I — shall — kiss your —

fp fp

(Masetto goes away again, but not so crossly; he even steals a few glances at Zerlina.)

Z.

ciar. Bat - ti, — batti o bel Ma -
hand. Do — not — spare me, dear Ma -

Str.

Wood Cor. sustain.

Z.

set - to, la tua po - ve - ra Zer - li - na! sta - rò qui come a - gnel -
set - to, Pun - ish — your Zer - li - na meet - ly; Like a lamb - kin, hum - bly,

(still trying to get one of Masetto's hands; he always draws back.)
Z.
li - na le tue botte ad a - spet - tar. O bel Ma-sèt-to!
sweet-ly, I re - pent-ant shall sub - mit. O dear Ma-set-to,
Wood
Bat - ti, bat-ti! sta-rò qui, sta-rò qui le tue botte ad a - spet-
do not spare me! I shall not weep a bit As re - pent-ant I sub-
tar. Ah, lo ve - do,
mit. Will you strike me?
Vln.
tr
non hai co - re, ah non hai
Can you bear to? Con-fess you
(here Zerlina seizes one of his hands.)
Allegro.
co - re, ah, lo ve - do, non hai co - re. Pa - ce, pa - ce, o vi - ta
love me! Do you dare to? Why re - sist me? Say that you are cross no
f
p
Cello
cresc.

Z.
mi - a! pa-ce, pa - ce,o vi - ta mi - a! in — con - ten - to ed al - le -
long - er! Though your wrath - be strong - as you are, You — know well — your love — is
Z.
gri - a not - te e dì — vo - gliam pas - sar,
strong - er, And — you love — me in — your heart,
Ob.
Fag.
Z.
not - te e dì — vo - gliam pas - sar, not - te e
And — for - give — me from — your heart, And for -
Wood.
Z.
dì — vo - gliam pas - sar, not - te e dì — vo - gliam pas -
give — me from — your heart, And for - give — me from — your
Z.
sar. Pa - ce, pa - ce,o vi - ta mi - a! Pa - ce, pa - ce,o vi - ta
heart. When our lips — and lives — u - nit - ed So com - plete - ly then — are
Str.

Z.

mi - a! in con - ten - to ed al - le - gri - a not - te e
hap - py, That all heav - en — seems de - light - ed, Can you

Fl. Fag.

Cor. sust.

(Masetto, quite persuaded, gazes joyfully on his bride.)

Z.

dì — vo - gliam — pas - sar, sì, sì, sì, sì, sì, sì, not - te e
keep — them still — a - part? No, no, no, no, no, no, You can

Z.

dì — vo - gliam pas - sar, sì, sì, sì, sì, sì, sì, not - te e dì — vo - gliam pas -
not — keep us — a - part. No, no, no, no, no, no, We can - not — re - main — a -

Z.

sar, — vo - gliam, vo - gliam pas - sar, — vo - gliam, vo - gliam pas -
part, — can - not — re - main — a - part, — can - not — re - main — a -

Z.

sar.
part.

pp

Recit.

Masetto. (gaily.)

M. Guarda un po', come seppe questa strega sedurmi! siamo
She's a bundle of witchcraft, and it's hopeless resisting! Is there

M. G. pure i deboli di testa!
really a man as strong as a woman?

Don Giovanni (within.)

Sia preparato tutto a una gran
We shall need more refreshments! New guests are

G. Z. festa.
coming!

Zerlina. (frightened.)

Ah, Masetto, Masetto, odi la voce del Mon-
Oh! Masetto, Masetto, I hear his lordship! If he

Z. M. sù Cavaliero!
comes to the garden...

Masetto. (suspiciously.)

Ebben, che c'è?
What's wrong with that?

Zerlina.

Verrà!
He'll see...

Masetto.

Lascia che
You and your

M. Z. venga.
bridegroom.

Zerlina.

Ah, se vi fosse un buco da fuggir!
If only I knew a place where we could hide!

Masetto.

Di cosa temi, per-
Why need we hide there? And

M. chè diventi pallida? Ah, capisco! capisco, bricconcella: hai ti-
why are you so terrified? Oh! I see now! How could I be so stupid! You're a-

(it gradually grows dark.)

M. mor ch'io comprenda com' è tra voi passata la faccenda.
fraid I'll discover just how untouched you *have* been by your lover!

Nº 13. "Presto, presto, pria ch'ei venga."

Finale.

Zerlina.

Z. (Ah, non gio - van le pa - ro - le!)
(How can I ex - plain it nice - ly?)

M. vuo - le. Par - la for - te, e qui t'ar -
cise - ly? Raise your voice for me to

p *cresc.* *f*

Z. Che ca - pric-cio ha nel - la te - sta, che ca - pric - cio ha nel - la
Low - er yours or he may hear you! Low - er yours or he may

M. re - sta! Par - la for - te, e qui t'ar -
hear you! Raise your voice for me to

p *cresc.* *cresc.*

Z. te - sta? *(sotto voce)* quell' in - gra - to, quel cru - de - le, og - gi
hear you! This is dread-ful, in - con - ven - ient. I'm a -

M. *(sotto voce)* re - sta! Ca - pi - rò se m'è fe - de - le, e in qual modo
hear you! I am done with be - ing le - nient: If she's faith-less,

p

Z. vuol pre - ci - pi - tar; quell' in - gra - to, quel cru - de - le, og - gi vuol pre - ci - pi -
fraid how things will go! This is dread - ful, in - con - ven - ient. I'm afraid how things will

M. an - dò l'affar! Ca - pi - rò se m'è fe - de - le,
I have to know! I am done with be - ing le - nient:

Z.
M.
G.
tar, quell' in-gra-to, quel cru-de-le,
go! This is dread-ful, in-con-ven-ient.
se m'è fe-de-le, e in qual mo-do an-dò l'af-far, in qual
If she is faith-less, If she's faith-less, I must know! If she's
oggi vuol pre-ci-pi-tar.
I'm a-fraid how things will go!
(Enter Don Giovanni with four gaily dressed servants)
mo-do an-dò l'af-far.
faith-less, I must know!
(Hides in the arbor)
Tutti
Don Giovanni. (to the peasants)
Sù! sve-glia-te-vi da bra-vi!
Let your watch-word be a-ban-don!
Sù! co-rag-gio, o buo-na gen-te! vogliam sta-re al-le-gra-men-te, vogliam ri-de-re, e scher-zar.
Be of care and time for-get-ful; Un-fore-bod-ing, un-re-gret-ful, Take your wine and take your love!
(to the servants)
Al-la stan-za del-la dan-za con-du-ce-te tut-ti
Take my guests at once and guide them To the ball-room and the

G.
quan-ti, ed a tut-ti a ab-bon-dan-za, gran rin-fre-schi fa-te
ta-bles; See re-fresh-ment is sup-plied them Ev-er bet-ter than e-
G.
dar! gran ri-fre-schi fa-te dar!
nough, Ev-er bet-ter than e-nough!
(Don Giovanni, looking everywhere for Zerlina, at last discovers her, and then gives Leporello a sign to take the peasants and servants into the villa)
cresc.
f
Chorus of Servants.
TENOR & BASS.
Sù, sve-glia-te-vi da bra-vi!
Let your watch-word be a-ban-don!
tr
Sù! co-rag-gio, o buo-na gen-te! vo-gliam sta-re al-le-gra-
Be of care and time for-get-ful! Un-fore-bod-ing, un-re-
3
men-te, vo-gliam ri-de-re, e scher-zar, Vo-gliam sta-re al-le-gra-
gret-ful, Take your love and take your wine! Un-fore-bod-ing, un-re-

(going off.)
men-te, vo-gliam ri-de-re e scher-zar, vo-gliam ri-de-re e scher-
gret-ful, Take your love and take your wine! Take your love and take your
(exit.)
zar, vo-gliam ri-de-re e scher-zar, vo-gliam
wine! Take your love and take your wine! Take your
poco a poco piano
Andante.
Zerlina (trying to hide herself.)
Z.
Tra quest'
Kind-ly
(exeunt peasants.)
ri-de-re e scher-zar!
love and take your wine!
Andante.
Vln.
p
Z.
ar-bo-ri-ce-la-ta, si può dar che non mi
shad-ow, lend me ha-ven From my fear and my temp-
Don Giovanni.
(detains her.)
Z.
G.
ve-da. Zer-li-net-ta, mia gar-ba-ta,
ta-tion. Still, my love, so fond-ly cra-ven...
Cor.
f

Zerlina. (trying to escape).

G. Z.

t'ho già vi-sto, t'ho già vi - sto, non scap-par. Ah, la-scia - te-mi andar

Must you, must you From your for-tune ev - er fly? Let me go, sir, please, I

p

Don Giovanni. Zerlina.

Z. G. Z.

vi - a! No, no, re - sta, gio - ja mi - a! Se pie - ta - de a-ve-te in

dare not. Can you see my pain and care not? May not no - ble pit - y

Don Giovanni. (indicating the arbor, which

Z. G.

co - re_ Sì, ben mio, son tut - to a - mo - re; vie - - - ni un

move you? Pit - y me, who can but love you. Warm - - - ly

he approaches backwards, drawing Zerlina after him)

G.

po - co in que - - sto lo - co! for - - tu - na - ta io ti vo'

in that shade de - light-ing, Ev - - er let our_ sor - rows

Zerlina.

Z.

Ah! sei ve - de il spo - - so mi - o, so ben

If Ma - set - to were to find us, I could

G.

far! vie - ni un po - - co in que - sto lo - - co, for - tu -

die!_ Warm - ly in_ that shade de - light - - ing, Ev - er

Z. io quel che può far, sò ben io, sò ben io, sò quel che può
not do less than die! O why must you So shake my heart, why O

G. na-ta io ti vo' far! for-tu-na-ta io ti vo'
let our sor-rows die, Ev-er let our sor-rows

Z. far, sò ben io, sò ben io, sò quel che può far!
why? O why must you So shake my heart, why O why?

G. far! for-tu-na-ta io ti vo' far!
die. Ev-er let our sor-rows die!

Str. & Corni

(Don Giovanni goes towards the arbor, sees Masetto, and stands petrified.)

M. **Masetto.** Sì, Ma-set-to!
Yes, Ma-set-to!

G. Ma-set-to? **Don Giovanni.** (a little confused) E
Ma-set-to? We're

G. chiu-so là, per-chè? (recovering himself) La bel-la tua Zer-
luck-y, it ap-pears... Zer-li-na felt de-

G.
li - na non può, la po-ve-ri - na, più
ject - ed At be - - ing so ne-glect - ed; She
star sen - za di te, non può più star sen - za di
came to me in tears And begged my help in find - ing
cresc.
p
tr
Masetto. (ironically)
Don Giovanni.
G.
M.
G.
te. Ca-pi-sco, sì, Si - gno - re. A - des - so fa - te
you. I'm sor - ry, sir and grate - ful too. It's I who should be
Cl.
cresc.
p
f
Allegretto.
(steps between Masetto and Zerlina, giving each an arm).
co - re, fa - te co - re. I suo-na-to-ri u - di - te, ve -
grate-ful, ver-y grate-ful, For now you both to-geth-er Can
Quartet, Ob. and horns
(on stage, at a distance)
Zerlina.
Z.
Sì, sì, fac-cia-mo co - re, sì, sì, fac-cia-mo
Yes, let us go to-geth-er And join in mak-ing
Masetto.
G.
M.
ni - te o - mai con me! Sì, sì, fac-cia-mo
join the dance with me! And join in mak-ing
p Orchestra

Z.
co-re, ed a bal-lar co-gli al-tri an-dia-mo tut-ti tre, an-
mer-ry... To mu-sic and to danc-ing We al-ways can a-gree! To
Don Giovanni.
G.
Ve-ni-te o-mai, ve-ni-te o-mai con me, ve-
Come join the dance, Come join the dance with me! To
M.
co-re, ed a bal-lar co-gli al-tri an-dia-mo tut-ti tre, an-
mer-ry... To mu-sic and to danc-ing We al-ways can a-gree! To
cresc.
f
dia-mo, an-dia-mo tut-ti tre, an-dia-mo, an-dia-mo
mu-sic and danc-ing We a-gree! To mu-sic and danc-ing
ni-te, ve-ni-te o-mai con me, ve-ni-te, ve-ni-te o-
mu-sic We al-ways can a-gree! To danc-ing We al-ways
dia-mo, an-dia-mo tut-ti tre, an-dia-mo, an-dia-mo
mu-sic and danc-ing We a-gree! To mu-sic and danc-ing
tut-ti tre, an-dia-mo tut-ti tre, an-dia-mo tut-ti tre!
We a-gree! To mu-sic We a-gree! To danc-ing We a-gree!
mai con me, ve-ni-te o-mai con me, ve-ni-te o-mai con me!
can a-gree! To mu-sic We a-gree! To danc-ing We a-gree!
tut-ti tre, an-dia-mo tut-ti tre, an-dia-mo tut-ti tre!
We a-gree! To mu-sic We a-gree! To danc-ing We a-gree! (Exeunt.)
(Enter Don Octavio, Donna Anna, and Donna Elvira, masked.)
Wind
Str.
p

Donna Elvira.
E.
Bi - sog - na a-ver co - rag-gio, o ca-ri a-mi-ci mie-i! e i
Nor should we lack in dar-ing; For all his shame-less cour-age, In
Vlns in 8ve
E.
O.
Don Octavio.
suoi mi-sfat-ti re - i sco - prir, sco - prir po - tre - mo al - lor. L'a -
truth re - sides our pow - er— The truth, the truth need nev - er wait! Dis -
O.
mi - ca di - ce be - ne! co - raggio a-ver con - vie - ne; di - scac-cia o vi - ta
cre - tion paired with dar - ing Would be our tru - est cour - age; Un - scru - pu - lous in
O.
mi - a, l'af - fan - no ed il ti - mor!
pow - er, His pow - er yet is great.
Corni sustain.
Donna Anna.
A.
Il pas - so è pe - ri - glio - so,
We know he slew my fath - er!
A.
può na - scer qual - che im - bro - glio.
We want no more than just - ice!
Str.

A.
Io te - mo pel ca - ro spo - so, pel
Why more need we now con - sid - er What
ca - ro spo-so, e per noi te - mo an - cor!
can - not al-ter— We were, we are... his fate!
te - mo pel ca - ro spo - so, pel ca - ro
Though I may fear his pow - er, Yet while I
Wood.
Fag.
spo - so, e per noi te - mo an - cor!
trem - ble I steel my heart with hate!
(Leporello opens the window from within.) Leporello.
L.
Menuetto. (in the distance, on the stage)
Si-gnor guar-da-te un po-co, che mas-che-re ga-
Sir, look who's just ar-rived here Some peo-ple masquer-
p
Don Giovanni. (at the window.)
L. G.
lan - ti! Fal - le pas-sar a-van - ti, di, che ci fan - no o-
ad - ing! Good! Just what we were need-ing — Ask them to join the

Donna Anna.
p (all three have seen Don Giovanni; aside).
A.
Al vol-to ed al-la vo-ce si sco-pre il tra-di-to-re!
(Re-gret-less, un-fore-bod-ing, He danc-es to per-di-tion!)
Donna Elvira.
E.
p
Al vol-to ed al-la vo-ce si sco-pre il tra-di-to-re!
(Re-gret-less, un-fore-bod-ing, He danc-es to per-di-tion!)
Don Octavio.
O.
p
Al vol-to ed al-la vo-ce si sco-pre il tra-di-to-re!
(Re-gret-less, un-fore-bod-ing, He danc-es to per-di-tion!)
G.
L.
nor!
ball.
Leporello.
Zi!
Psst!
Via ri-spon-de-te.
You'd bet-ter an-swer.
(to Don Octavio_softly.)
Via ri-spon-de-te.
You'd bet-ter an-swer.
zi! Si-gno-re ma-schere! Zi! zi!
Psst! You there in dom-in-o! Psst! Psst!
Zi!
Psst!
Don Octavio.
Co-sa chie-de-te?
I beg your par-don . . .
zi! Si-gno-re ma-schere!
Psst! You there in dom-in-o!
Al bal-lo, se vi
To danc-ing and re-

Don Octavio. (to Leporello). (to Donna Anna and D. Elvira)

L. O.

pia - ce, v'in - vi - ta il mio Si - gnor. Gra - zie di tan - to o - no - re! an - diam, compagne bel - le.
fresh - ment, My mas - ter bids you all. Tell him we should be hon - ored. Your arms, my gra - cious la - dies...

Leporello. (aside)

L'a - mi - co anche su quel - le pro - va fa - rà d'a - mor!
(He'd bet - ter watch his la - dies Lest in the list they fall!) Goes in and shuts the window)

Adagio.

Orchestra *p* Str.

Donna Anna. (all three unmask, and advance to front.)

A.

Pro - teg - ga il giu - sto cie - lo il ze - lo del mio cor! pro -
Im - mor - tal love, pro - tect us, Our hopes and wills u - nite. Our

Don Octavio.

Pro - teg - ga il giu - sto cie - lo il ze - lo del mio cor!
Im - mor - tal love, pro - tect us, Our hopes and wills u - nite.

Donna Elvira.

E.

Ven - di - chi il giu - sto cie - lo il mio tra - di - to a -
Mer - ci - ful God, in - spire me To know and want the

Wind.

A.
teg - ga il giu - - - sto cie - - - lo il
zeal, O God of just - - - ice, Re -
E.
mor, ven-di-chi il giu-sto cie-lo il mio tra-di-to a-
right! Right-ly may venge-ance sol-ace My love's dis-heart-ened
O.
pro-teg-ga il giu-sto cie-lo il ze-lo del mio
Our zeal, O God of just-ice, Re-gard, ap-prove, re-
Cl.
Fag.
A.
ze - - - - - - lo del mio cor, pro-
gard, ap-prove, re - quite! Im-
E.
mor, il mio tra - di-to, tra-di-to a - mor!
plight, My love's dis - heart-ened, dis-heart-ened plight!
O.
cor, il ze-lo il ze-lo del mio cor!
quite! Our zeal, Re - - gard, ap-prove, re - quite!
A.
teg - ga il giu - - sto cie - - - lo il
mor - tal love, pro - tect us, Our
E.
Ven-di-chi il giu-sto cie-lo il mio tra-di-to a-
Right-ly may venge-ance sol-ace My love's dis-heart-ened
O.
pro-teg-ga il giu-sto cie-lo il ze-lo del mio
Im-mor-tal love, pro-tect us, Our hopes and wills u-
Cl.

A.
ze - - - - lo del mio cor, pro-
hopes and wills u - nite. Our

E.
mor, il mio, il mio tra-di - to a-mor, ven-di-chi, ven-di-chi il giusto
plight, My love's, My love's dis-heart ened plight! Rightly O Rightly may vengeance

O.
cor, il zelo, il ze - lo del mio cor, pro-
nite. O God, Our hopes and wills u - nite. Our

A.
teg-ga il giu - sto cie-lo il ze - lo del mio
zeal, O God of just-ice, Re - gard, ap - prove, re-

E.
cie - lo il mio tra-di-to, tra-di-to a-mor, tra-di - to a-
sol - ace My love's disheartened dis-heartened plight, dis-heart - ened

O.
teg-ga il giu - sto cie-lo il ze - lo del mio
zeal, O God of just-ice, Re - gard, ap - prove, re-

A.
cor!
quite! (All resume their masks.)

E.
mor!
plight! (Exeunt.) (Scene changes to a brilliantly lighted ballroom.)

O.
cor!
quite!

Fag.
Ob
Fl.
Cl.
sfp

(Don Giovanni is handing some young girls to seats. Leporello is amongst the men; a dance is just over.)
Allegro.
Don Giovanni.
Ri-po-sa-te, vez-zo-se ra-gaz-ze!
Would you girls like to sit for a min-ute?
Leporello.
Rin-fre-sca-te-vi, bei gio-vi-
Won't you men have a lit-tle re-
Tor-ne-re-te a far presto le paz-ze, tor-ne-re-te a scher-zar e bal-
Your ver-tig-i-nous joy you must length-en In the strength-en-ing joy of re-
net-ti! Tor-ne-re-te a far presto le paz-ze, tor-ne-re-te a scher-zar e bal-
fresh-ment? Your ver-tig-i-nous joy you must length-en In the strength-en-ing joy of re-
lar, a scher-zar e bal-lar!
pose, Then be back on your toes!
(to the servants)
Ehi, Caf-fè! (Refreshments are handed.)
Mus-ca-tel!
lar, a scher-zar e bal-lar!
pose, Then be back on your toes!
Vln.
cresc.

Leporello.
Masetto.(holding Zerlina anxiously by her gown)
Don Giovanni.
L.
M.
G.
Cioc-co-la-te! Ah, Zer-li-na! giu-di-zio! Sor-
Bring the choc-lates! Now Zer-li-na, be cau-tious! The
Wind.
Vln.
Leporello.
Masetto.
G.
L.
M.
bet-ti! Con-fet-ti! Ah, Zer-li-na! giu-di-zio!
al-monds! The ic-es! Now Zer-li-na, be cau-tious!
Zerlina. (aside in great confusion).
Z.
Trop-po dol-ce co-min-cia la sce-na, in a-
Though I fear such a lav-ish be-gin-ning May por-
Masetto. (aside)
M.
Trop-po dol-ce co-min-cia la sce-na, in a-
Though I fear such a lav-ish be-gin-ning May por-
tr
Z.
ma-ro po-tria ter-mi-nar, sì, in a-ma-ro po-
tend some im-prov-i-dent end, Yet To re-sist might be
M.
ma-ro po-tria ter-mi-nar, sì, in a-ma-ro po-
tend some im-prov-i-dent end, Yet To re-sist might be

Zerlina. (smiling shyly)
Z.
tria ter-mi-nar! Sua bon-
thought to of-fend. How you
Don Giovanni. (caressingly.)
M.
G.
tria ter-mi-nar! Sei pur va-ga, brillan-te Zer-li-na!
thought to of-fend. You, Zer-li-na, grow ev-er more win-ning.
Wind.
Vlns
Cl.
Fag.
Leporello. (Amongst the girls, imitating his master.)
Z.
L.
tà! Sei pur ca-ra, Gia-not-ta, San-dri-na!
talk! Ev-er win-ning, Gian-not-ta, San-dri-na!
Masetto. (aside, enraged)
M.
La bric-co-na fa fe-sta! Toc-ca
She has not learned her les-son. When her
Zerlina. (aside; looking at Masetto).
Z.
Quel Ma-set-to mi par stra-lu-na-to, brut-to,
I don't like how Ma-set-to is watch-ing, I'm a-
M.
pur, che ti ca-da la te-sta.
hol-i-day's o-ver she'll catch it!
cresc.
Z.
brut-to si fa quest' af-far! Quel Ma-set-to mi par stra-lu-
fraid how Ma-set-to will act. I don't like how Ma-set-to is
Don Giovanni. (aside)
G.
Quel Ma-set-to mi par stra-lu-na-to,
I don't like how Ma-set-to is watch-ing
Leporello. (aside)
L.
Quel Ma-set-to mi par stra-lu-na-to,
I don't like how Ma-set-to is watch-ing,
f
p

Z.
na - to!
watch-ing,
Brut - to, brut - to si fa — quest'af -
I'm a - fraid — how — Ma - set - to — will
G.
Qui bi - so - gna cer - vel - lo a - do - prar.
This af - fair must be man - aged with tact.
L.
Qui bi - so - gna cer - vel - lo a - do - prar.
Masetto. (growing angrier.)
This af - fair must be man - aged with tact.
M.
La bric - co - na fa fe - sta!
She will bear with some watch - ing!
Wind.
Vln.
Z.
far!
act.
Quel Ma - set - to mi par stra - lu -
I don't like how Ma - set - to is
G.
Quel Ma - set - to mi par stra - lu -
I don't like how Ma - set - to is
Masetto.
M.
L.
Lep.
Toc - ca pur, che ti ca - da la te - sta! Quel Ma - set - to mi par stra - lu -
When her hol - i - day's o - ver she'll catch it. I don't like how Ma - set - to is
f
p
Z.
na - to, brut - to, brut - to si fa quest'af - far, si fa quest' af - far! quel Ma -
watch - ing, I'm a - fraid how Ma - set - to will act — When will he have tact? I don't
G.
na - to, qui bi - so - gna cer - vel - lo a - do - prar, cer - vel - lo a - do - prar! quel Ma -
watch - ing, This af - fair must be man - aged with tact, And that is a fact! I don't
L.
na - to, qui bi - so - gna cer - vel - lo a - do - prar, cer - vel - lo a - do - prar! quel Ma -
watch - ing, This af - fair must be man - aged with tact, And that is a fact! I don't
Masetto.
M.
Toc - ca, toc - ca!
She will catch it!
f
p
cresc.
f
p

Z.
set-to mi par stralu - na - to, brutto, brut-to si fa quest' af - far, si
like how Ma-set-to is watch - ing, I'm a-fraid how Ma-set-to will act. When
G.
set-to mi par stralu - na - to, qui bi - sogna cervello a-do - prar, cer-
like how Ma-set-to is watch - ing, This af-fair must be man-aged with tact, And
L.
set-to mi par stralu - na - to, qui bi - sogna cervello a-do - prar, cer-
like how Ma-set-to is watch - ing, This af-fair must be man-aged with tact, And
M.
Ah bricco - na! ah bric-co - na! mi
She bears watch-ing For the trou - ble she
f
p
cresc.
Z.
fa quest' af - far, brut-to, brut - to si fa quest' af - far!
will he have tact? I'm a - fraid how Ma - set - to will act.
G.
vel - lo a-do - prar, qui bi - so - gna cer-vel - lo a-do-prar!
that is a fact! This af - fair must be man-aged with tact.
L.
vel - lo a-do - prar, qui bi - so - gna cer-vel - lo a-do-prar!
that is a fact! This af - fair must be man-aged with tact.
(Enter Don Octavio, Donna Anna, and Donna Elvira, masked.)
M.
vuoi di - spe - rar; ah bric-co - na! mi vuoi di-spe-rar!
loves to at-tract, For the trou - ble she loves to at-tract!
p
Maestoso.
L.
Leporello. (to the three.)
Ve - ni - te pur a - van-ti, vez - zo - se ma-sche-
Per - mit me, for my mas - ter, To wel-come you with
Tutti.
tr
Str.
Wind.
p

L.
G.
Don Giovanni. (saluting them.)
ret-te! È a-per-to a tut-ti quan-ti,
pleas-ure. Your pleas-ure be as you will;
tr
f Tromb.
p
fp
Donna Anna. (curtseying.)
A.
Siam gra-ti a tan-ti se-gni di ge-ne-ro-si-
How no-ble is your kind-ness To us and ev-'ry
Donna Elvira.
E.
Siam gra-ti a tan-ti se-gni di ge-ne-ro-si-
How no-ble is your kind-ness To us and ev-'ry
Don Octavio. (bowing.)
G.
O.
vi-va la li-ber-tà. Siam gra-ti a tan-ti se-gni di ge-ne-ro-si-
And what you will, be done. How no-ble is your kind-ness To us and ev-'ry
tà, di ge-ne-ro-si-tà; siam gra-ti
one, To us and ev-'ry one! How no-ble...
tà, di ge-ne-ro-si-tà; siam gra-ti
one, To us and ev-'ry one! How no-ble...
tà, di ge-ne-ro-si-tà; siam gra-ti
one, To us and ev-'ry one! How no-ble...
Don Giovanni.
È a-per-to a tut-ti, a tut-ti
All do as they will... That is the
f

A.
a tan-ti se-gni di ge-ne-ro-si-tà!
You show your kind-ness To us and ev-'ry one!
E.
a tan-ti se-gni di ge-ne-ro-si-tà!
You show your kind-ness To us and ev-'ry one!
O.
a tan-ti se-gni di ge-ne-ro-si-tà!
You show your kind-ness To us and ev-'ry one!
G.
quanti,
law here!
vi-va, vi-va la li-ber-tà!
Do what you will is our on-ly law.
Strings Corni Fag. & Tympani.
p
mf
f
(servants place three-chairs at left, front.)
Donna Anna.
A.
E.
Donna Elvira.
Vi-va la li-ber-tà! la li-ber-tà,
All that you may de-sire, May here be done!
Don Octavio.
O.
Vi-va la li-ber-tà! la li-ber-tà,
All that you may de-sire, May here be done!
Don Giovanni.
G.
Vi-va la li-ber-tà! la li-ber-tà,
All that you may de-sire, May here be done!
Leporello.
L.
Vi-va la li-ber-tà! la li-ber-tà,
All that you may de-sire, May here be done!

A.
E.
Vi-va la li-ber-tà, la li-ber-tà, vi-va,
All that you may de-sire May here be done! Do as
O.
Vi-va la li-ber-tà, la li-ber-tà, vi-va,
All that you may de-sire May here be done! Do as
G.
Vi-va la li-ber-tà, la li-ber-tà, vi-va,
All that you may de-sire May here be done! Do as
L.
Vi-va la li-ber-ta, la li-ber-tà, vi-va,
All that you may de-sire May here be done! Do as
A.
E.
vi-va la li-ber-tà, vi-va, vi-va la li-ber-tà, la li-ber-tà, la li-ber-
thou wilt, is here the law! Do as thou wilt, is here the law! Thy will be done, thy will be
O.
vi-va la li-ber-tà, vi-va, vi-va la li-ber-tà, la li-ber-tà, la li-ber-
thou wilt, is here the law! Do as thou wilt, is here the law! Thy will be done, thy will be
G.
vi-va la li-ber-tà, vi-va, vi-va la li-ber-tà, la li-ber-tà, la li-ber-
thou wilt, is here our law! Do as thou wilt, is here our law! Thy will be done, thy will be
L.
vi-va la li-ber-tà, vi-va, vi-va la li-ber-tà, la li-ber-tà, la li-ber-
thou wilt, is here our law! Do as thou wilt, is here our law! Thy will be done, thy will be

*) These two phrases in small notes are not included in the score, but are found in the earliest copied voice-parts, and were probably inserted at the first rehearsals.

Donna Anna. (agitatedly, to Don Octavio.)
Io mo-ro!
He's with her!
di-na.
told you . . .
Don Octavio. (to Donna Anna.)
Si - mu - la - te.
Hide your feel-ings!
Don Giovanni.
Va be - ne in ve - ri - tà!
How smooth - ly things com - bine!
Leporello.
Masetto. (ironically.)
Va be - ne in ve - ri - tà! Va be - ne, va
How smooth - ly things com - bine! How smooth-ly, how
(To Leporello.)
A ba-da tien Ma-set-to.
Take care of our Ma-set-to.
be - ne, va bene in ve - ri - tà!
smooth-ly, How smooth-ly things com-bine.
(to Zerlina.)
Il tuo compagno io so - no, Zer-
Zer-li - na, when I hold you, I
Leporello. (compassionately, to Masetto.)
Non bal-li, po - ve - ret - to, po-ve-ret-to!
Don't stand there stiff and froz-en, Don't be bash-ful
Vien quà Ma-set - to
Come join The oth-ers,

(embraces her, and tries to kiss her; Zerlina opposes him, escapes, and hides behind the dancers.)
G.
li - na, Zer - li - na, vien pur quà!
trem - ble . . . O grant me one small kiss!
(crossly, opposing him.)
Masetto.
L.
M.
ca - ro, ca - ro! fac-ciam quel ch'altri fa. No, no, ballar non
dear Ma-set - to, It's too much fun to miss! No, no! I do not
Leporello.
Masetto.
Leporello. (turning him.)
M.
L.
vo-glio! Eh, bal - la, ami - co mi - o! No! Sì!
want to! You know you real - ly want to! No! Yes!
Donna Anna.
A.
Re-si - ster non poss' i - o!
I can no-more-dis - sem-ble!
Donna Elvira.
E.
Fin-ge - te per pie -
You must, a lit - tle
Don Octavio.
O.
Fin-ge - te per pie -
You must, a lit - tle
Leporello.
Masetto.
Leporello.
Masetto.
L.
M.
ca-ro Ma-set-to! Bal - la! No, no, non vo - glio! Bal-la! No, no, non
You know you want to— don't you? I know I will not! Won't you? I won't! I

F.
tà! (Zerlina, passing between the dancers, has gradually approached the door at right; here Don
while! Giovanni reaches her, puts his arm about her waist, and draws her towards the door.)
O.
tà!
while!
Leporello.
M.
L.
vo - glio. Eh, bal - la, ami - co mi - o! fac - ciam quel ch'al - tri
tell you! You force me to com - pel — you To dance a — bit and
Don Giovanni.
G.
Vie - ni con me, — mia vi - ta! vie - ni,
Heart of my heart, — I need you, Need you
Masetto. (struggling.)
L.
M.
fa. La - scia - mi! Ah no! Zer -
smile! (Forces Masetto to dance with him.) Let me by! You hear! Zer -
Donna Anna.
A.
L'i -
Now
Zerlina.
Z.
E.
O nu - mi! son tra - di - ta.
O don't, sir! All these peo - ple . . .
Donna Elvira.
L'i -
Now
Don Octavio.
G.
O.
vie - ni!
too much! (Leads her off against her will.)
L'i -
Now
Leporello.
M.
L.
li - na!
li - na!
Qui nasce u - na ru - i - na.
The cat - alogue is growing.
(Exit hastily after them.)

A.
ni - quo da se stes - so nel lac - cio se ne va!
soon the vile in - trigu - er Will be ex-posed as vile!
E.
ni - quo da se stes - so nel lac - cio se ne va!
soon the vile in - trigu - er Will be ex-posed as vile!
O.
ni - quo da se stes - so nel lac - cio se ne va!
soon the vile in - trigu - er Will be ex-posed as vile!
Allegro assai.
Donna Anna & Donna Elvira.
A.
E.
Soc-cor-
Quick-ly,
Zerlina. (from within.)
Z.
Gen - te, a - ju - to, a-ju - to! gen-te!
Help me, ev - 'ry bod - y, help me!
Don Octavio.
O.
(Tumult. The stage-orchestras cease, the main orchestra recommences.)
Soc-cor-
Quick-ly,
Allegro assai.
sfp
fp
(all turn towards door.)
A.
E.
ria-mo l'in-no-cen-te, Soc-cor-ria-mo l'in-no - cen-te!
quick-ly we must save her, Quick-ly, quick-ly we must save her.
O.
ria-mo l'in-no-cen-te, Soc-cor-ria-mo l'in-no - cen-te!
quick-ly we must save her, Quick-ly, quick-ly we must save her.
Masetto. (terri-
M.
Ah, Zer-
O Zer-
fp
fp
fp
p
cresc.

(her voice is heard at the other side.)
Zerlina.
Donna Anna & Donna Elvira.
Scel - le - ra - to! O - ra
Let me go! Quick-ly,
Don Octavio.
O - ra
Quick-ly,
bly excited.)
li - na, ah Zer - li - na!
li - na! O Zer - li - na!
p
cresc.
(all hasten to the door.)
gri - da da quel la - to, da quel la - to!
quick-ly to the door Through which he took her!
Zerlina.
Sce - le - ra -
Let me go!
gri - da da quel la - to, da quel la - to!
quick-ly to the door Through which he took her!
cresc.
Donna Anna & Donna Elvira.
Zerlina.
to! Ah git - tia - mo giù la por - ta, giù la por - ta! Soc-cor -
Quick-ly, quick - ly break the door down If it's bolt - ed! I can
Don Octavio.
Ah git - tia - mo giù la por - ta, giù la por - ta!
Quick-ly, quick - ly break the door down If it's bolt - ed!
f
p

re - te - mi! Ah soc - co - re - - temi! son
fight no more! Can no - one save me from this
cresc.
(They try to force the door.)
Donna Anna.
Siam qui noi per tua di -
We are com - ing to your
Donna Elvira.
Siam qui noi per tua di -
We are com - ing to your
Don Octavio.
mor - - - - ta! Siam qui noi per tua di -
dev - - - - il? We are com - ing to your
Masetto.
Siam qui noi per tua di -
We are com - ing to your
f
fe - sa, siam qui noi per tua di - fe - sa, per tua di -
res - cue! We are com - ing to your res - cue! A mo - ment
fe - sa, siam qui noi per tua di - fe - sa, per tua di -
res - cue! We are com - ing to your res - cue! A mo - ment
fe - sa, siam qui noi per tua di - fe - sa, per tua di -
res - cue! We are com - ing to your res - cue! A mo - ment
fe - sa, siam qui noi per tua di - fe - sa, per tua di -
res - cue! We are com - ing to your res - cue! A mo - ment

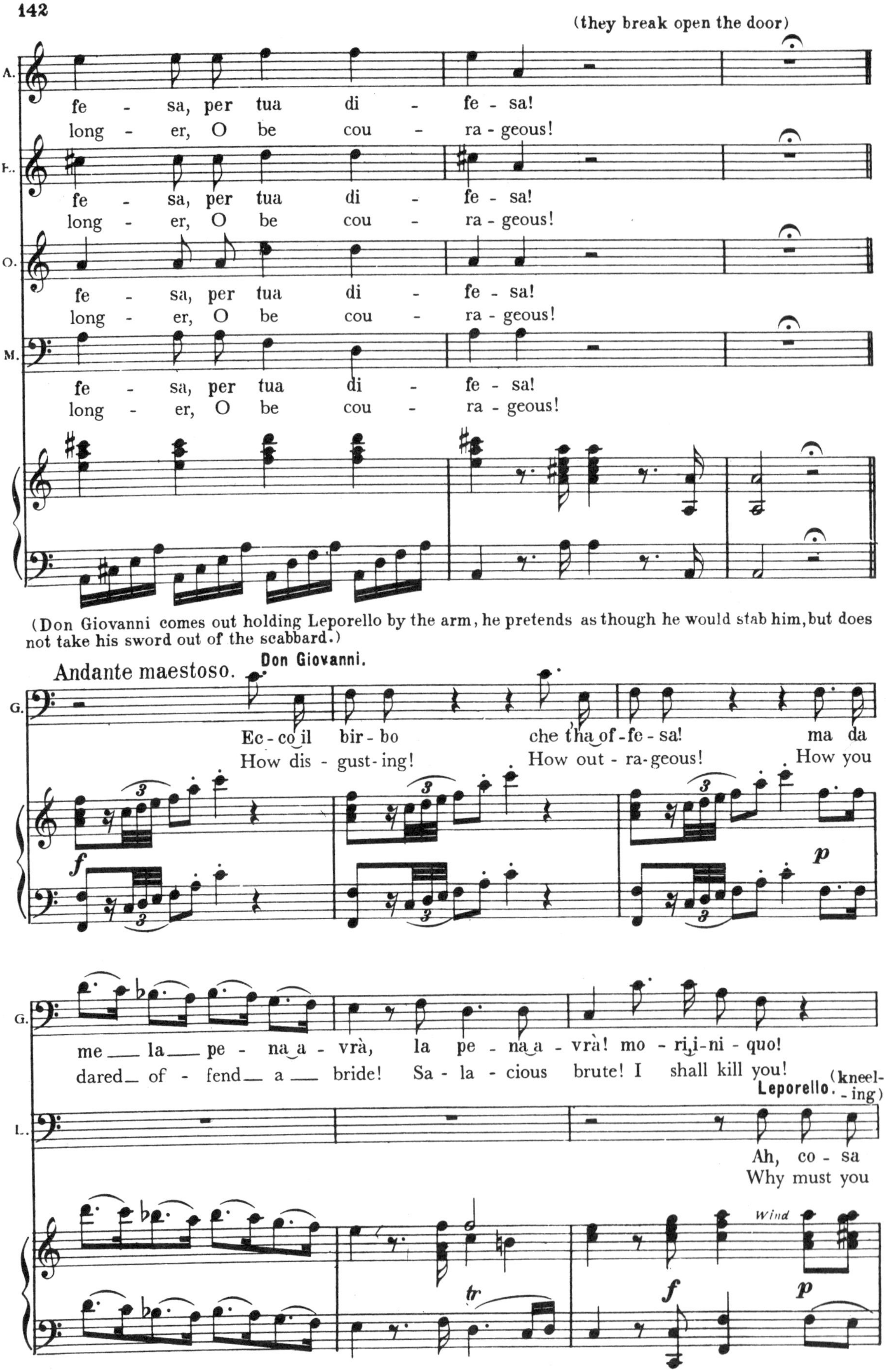

(Don Giovanni comes out holding Leporello by the arm, he pretends as though he would stab him, but does not take his sword out of the scabbard.)

Andante maestoso.

Don Giovanni.

G.
Ec - co il bir - bo che t'ha of - fe - sa! ma da
How dis - gust - ing! How out - ra - geous! How you

f *p*

G.
me — la — pe — na a - vrà, la pe - na a - vrà! mo - ri i - ni - quo!
dared — of - fend — a — bride! Sa - la - cious brute! I shall kill you!

Leporello. (kneel - ing)

L.
Ah, co - sa
Why must you

tr *f* *p* Wind

G.
mo - ri, di - co! mo - ri, di - co!
Flout me, will you? You de-serve none!
L.
fa - te! ah co - sa fa - te! ah co - sa
scare me? At least have mer - cy! O mas - ter,
f p f p
Don Octavio (taking out a pistol; to Don Giovanni.)
O.
No! spe-ra - te! nol spe - ra - te!
You'll re-lease him, Don Gio - van - ni!
L.
fa - te!
spare me!
cresc.
f
Donna Elvira.
(unmasking)
E.
L'em - pio cre - de con tal
No mere farce will un - con -
Don Octavio. (unmasking)
O.
L'em - pio cre - de con tal fro - de, con tal
No mere farce will un - con - vince us . . . Un - con -
fp fp
Donna Anna. (unmasking)
A.
L'em - pio cre - de con tal fro - de di nascon - der l'em - pie -
No mere farce will un - con - vince us Of the guilt you can - not
E.
fro - de, con tal fro - de di nascon - der l'em - pie -
vince us . . . un - con - vince us Of the guilt you can - not
O.
fro - de, con tal fro - de di nascon - der l'em - pie -
vince us . . . un - con - vince us Of the guilt you can - not
fp

A. tà, l'em - - pie - tà!
hide, Can - - not hide!

E. tà, l'em - - pie - tà! Sì, mal-vaggio!
hide, Can - - not hide! One who knows you!

O. tà, l'em - - pie - tà! Sì, si -
hide, Can - - not hide! Yes, your

G. (disconcerted, lets Leporello go)
Donna El-vi-ra? Don Ottavio?
Donn'El-vi-ra? Don Oc-ta-vio?

Wind. Strs. *p* *f*

Donna Anna.
A. Tra - di - to - re, tra - di - to - re, tra - di - to - re!
See your judg-es Here to-geth - er to ex-pose you!

Donna Elvira.
E. Tra - di-to - re, tra - di - to - re!
Here to-geth - er to ex-pose you!

Zerlina.
Z. Tra - di-to - re, tra - di - to - re! Tut - to,
Here to-geth - er to ex-pose you! All is

Don Octavio.
O. gno-re. Tra - di-to - re, tra - di - to - re!
lord-ship. Here to-geth - er to ex-pose you!

Don Giovanni.
G. (to Donna Anna) Ah credete!
Why this in-trigue?

Masetto.
M. Tra - di-to - re, tra - di - to - re!
Here to-geth - er to ex-pose you!

f *Strs. Wind sustain* *p*

A.
Tut - to,tut - to già si sa,
All is known and all shall know,
E.
Tut - to,tut - to già si sa,
All is known and all shall know,
Z.
tut - to già si sà, tut - to, tut - to già si
known and all shall know, All is known and all shall
O.
Tut - to,tut - to già si sa,
All is known and all shall know,
M.
Tut-to, tut - to già si sa, tut - to
All is known and all shall know, All is
A.
tut - to,tut - to già si sa, tut-to, tut - to già si
All man-kind shall be your foe, That un-ho - ly Thing you
E.
tut - to,tut - to già si sa, tut-to, tut - to già si
All man-kind shall be your foe, That un-ho - ly Thing you
Z.
sà, tut - to, tut - to già si sa, già si
know, All man-kind shall be your foe, What you
O.
tut - to,tut - to già si sa, tut-to,
All man-kind shall be your foe, What you
M.
tut - to già si sa,
known and all shall know,

A.
sa, tut - to, tut - to, tut - to, tut - to già si
are, earn you ha - tred Ev - 'ry - where you dare to
E.
sa, tut - to, tut - to, tut - to, tut - to già si
are, earn you ha - tred Ev - 'ry - where you dare to
Z.
sa, tut - to, tut - to, tut - to, tut - to già si
are, earn you ha - tred Ev - 'ry - where you dare to
O.
tut - to già si sa, tut - to, tut - to già si
are shall earn you hate Ev - 'ry - where you dare to
M.
tut - to, tut - to già si sa, tut - to, tut - to già si
Earn you ha - tred Ev - 'ry - where, ev - 'ry where you dare to
cresc.
(All the men threateningly approach Don Giovanni, who calmly awaits them, leaning on his sword)
A.
sa, tut-to! tut-to! tut - to!
go! Ha-tred! Ha-tred! Ha - tred!
E.
sa, tut-to! tut-to! tut - to!
go! Ha-tred! Ha-tred! Ha - tred!
Z.
sa, tut-to! tut-to! tut - to!
go! Ha-tred! Ha-tred! Ha - tred!
O.
sa, tut-to! tut-to! tut - to!
go! Ha-tred! Ha-tred! Ha - tred!
M.
sa, tut-to! tut-to! tut - to!
go! Ha-tred! Ha-tred! Ha - tred!

Allegro
Donna Anna and Zerlina.
A.
Z.
p
cresc.
Tre - ma, tre - ma,
Trem - ble as your
Donna Elvira.
E.
Tre - ma, tre - ma,
Trem - ble as your
Don Octavio.
O.
Tre - ma, tre - ma,
Trem - ble as your
Masetto.
M.
Tre - ma, tre - ma,
Trem - ble as your
Allegro
f
scel - le - ra-to! tre - ma,
end ap-proach-es! Trem - ble
Don Giovanni.
G.
sotto voce
È con-fu - sa la mia te-sta.
What a tem-pest! How like fu-ries!
Leporello.
L.
sotto voce
È con-fu - sa la sua te-sta.
What a tem-pest! How like fu-ries!
Masetto.
sce - le - ra-to! tre - ma,
end ap-proach-es! Trem - ble
tr

A. Z.
tre - ma, scel - - le - ra - to, sa - prà
as your end ap - proach-es! Now sur-
E.
tre - ma, scel - - le - ra - to, sa - prà
as your end ap - proach-es! Now sur-
O.
tre - ma, scel - - le - ra - to, sa - prà
as your end ap - proach-es! Now sur-
G.
Non sò più quel ch'io mi
They de - light in my dam-
L.
Non sa più quel ch'ei si
They de - light in his dam-
M.
tre - ma, sce - - le ra - to, sa - prà
as your end ap - proach - es! Now sur-
f
tr
p
D. Anna, D. Elvira and Zerlina.
A. E. Z.
to - sto il mon - do in - te - ro il mi - sfat - to or - ren - do e ne - ro, la tua
round-ed, shamed and thwart-ed, Know that doom was all you court-ed, Where your
Don Octavio.
O.
to - sto il mon - do in - te - ro il mi - sfat - to or - ren - do e ne - ro, la tua
round-ed, shamed and thwart-ed, Know that doom was all you court-ed, Where your
G.
fac - cia, e un or - ri - bi - le tem - pe - sta mi - nac - ciando, o Dio, mi
na - tion! What an awk-ward sit - u - a - tion! How I wish I were in
L.
fac - cia, e un or - ri - bi - le tem - pe - sta mi - nac - ciando, o Dio, lo
na - tion! What an awk-ward sit - u - a - tion! How I wish I were in
M.
to - sto il mon - do in - te - ro il mi - sfat - to or - ren - do e ne - ro, la tua
round-ed, shamed and thwart-ed, Know that doom was all you court-ed, Where your

A.
E.
Z.
fie-ra_cru-del-tà, la tua fie - ra cru - del-tà!
lust_has_ev - er_led All the life that you have led!
O.
fie-ra cru-del-tà, la tua fie - ra cru - del-tà!
lust_has_ev - er_led All the life that you have led!
G.
va! È con-fu - sa
bed! What a tem-pest!
L.
va! È con-
bed! What a
M.
fie-ra_cru-del-tà, la tua fie - ra cru - del-tà!
lust_has_ev - er_led All the life that you have led!
cresc.
p
A.
E.
Z.
Tre - ma! tre - ma!
Jus - tice! Jus - tice!
O.
Tre - ma! tre - ma!
Jus - tice! Jus - tice!
G.
la mia te - sta, non sò più quel ch'io mi fac-cia, e un or -
How like fu-ries! They de-light in my dam-na-tion! What an
L.
fu - sa la sua te - sta, non sa più quel ch'ei si fac - cia, e un or-
tem- pest! How like fu - ries! They de-light in his dam-na-tion! What an
M.
Tre - ma! tre - ma!
Jus - tice! Jus - tice!
Vlns
cresc.

Donna Anna and Zerlina.
A.
Z.
tre - ma, tre - - -
Donna Elvira.
For your crimes
E.
tre - ma, tre - ma, tre - ma,
Don Octavio.
Jus - tice, jus - tice for the
O.
tre - ma, tre - ma, tre - ma,
Jus - tice, jus - tice for the
G.
ri - bi-le tem-pe-sta mi - nac - cian - do, o Dio, mi va.
awk-ward sit - u-a-tion! How I wish I were in bed!
L.
ri - bi-le tem-pe-sta mi - nac - cian - do, o Dio, lo va.
awk-ward sit - u-a-tion! How I wish I were in bed!
M.
tre - ma, tre - ma, tre - ma,
Jus - tice, jus - tice for the
f
A.
Z.
- - ma scel - le - ra - to!
re - venge ap-proach-es!
E.
tre - ma, o scel - le - ra - to!
crimes, Of your life ap-proach-es!
O.
tre - ma, o scel - le - ra - to!
crimes, Of your life ap-proach-es!
G.
È con - fu - sa la mia te-sta, non sò più quel ch'io mi
What a tem-pest! How like fu-ries! They de-light in my dam-
L.
È con - fu - sa la sua te-sta, non sa più quel ch'ei si
What a tem-pest! How like fu-ries! They de-light in his dam-
M.
tre - ma, o sce - le - ra - to!
crimes, Of your life ap-proach-es!

D. Anna, D. Elvira and Zerlina.
A. E. Z.
O - di il tuon del-la ven - detta!
Mark the voice of wrath e - ter-nal!
Don Octavio.
O.
O - di il tuon del-la ven - detta!
Mark the voice of wrath e - ter-nal!
G.
faccia, e un or-ri - bi - le tempe-sta minacciando, o Dio, mi
na-tion! What an awk-ward sit-u - a-tion! How I wish I were in
L.
faccia, e un or-ri - bi - le tempe-sta minacciando, o Dio, lo
na-tion! What an awk-ward sit-u - a-tion! How I wish I were in
M.
O - di il tuon del-la ven - detta!
Mark the voice of wrath e - ter-nal!
tr
3
A. E. Z.
O - di il tuon del - la ven - det-ta, che ti fi-schia in-tor - no in
Mark the voice of wrath e - ter-nal! To our own, ac - cord is
O.
O - di il tuon del - la ven - det-ta, che ti fi-schia in-tor - no in
Mark the voice of wrath e - ter-nal! To our own, ac - cord is
G.
va! (Don Giovanni, behind whom Leporello shelters himself, attempts to clear a path for himself with
bed! his sword, but is hindered by Don Octavio.)
L.
va!
bed!
M.
O - di il tuon del - la ven - det-ta, che ti fi-schia in-tor - no in
Mark the voice of wrath e - ter-nal! To our own, ac - cord is
tr

A.
E.
Z.
tor - no, sul tuo ca-po in que - sto gior - no il suo ful - mi - ne ca -
giv - en: Mor - tal venge-ance armed by Heav - en Soon must fall up - on your
O.
tor - no, sul tuo ca-po in que - sto gior - no il suo ful - mi - ne ca -
giv - en: Mor - tal venge-ance armed by Heav - en Soon must fall up - on your
M.
tor - no, sul tuo ca-po in que - sto gior - no il suo ful - mi - ne ca -
giv - en: Mor - tal venge-ance armed by Heav - en Soon must fall up - on your
A.
E.
Z.
drà, il suo ful - mi - ne ca - drà!
head, Soon must fall up - on your head!
O.
drà, il suo ful - mi - ne ca - drà!
head, Soon must fall up - on your head!
Don Giovanni.
G.
È con-fu - sa la mia te - sta,
What a tem-pest! How like fu-ries!
Leporello.
L.
È con-fu - sa la sua
What a tem-pest! How like
Masetto.
M.
drà, il suo ful - mi - ne ca - drà!
head, Soon must fall up - on your head!
p

A.
E.
Z.
tre - ma! tre - ma!
Venge-ance! Venge-ance!
O.
tre - ma! tre - ma!
Venge-ance! Venge-ance!
G.
non sò più quel ch'io mi fac - cia, e un or - - ri - bi - le tem-
They de-light in my dam-na-tion! What an awk - ward sit - u-
L.
te - sta, non sa più quel ch'ei si fac - cia, e un or - ri - bi - le tem-
fu - ries! They de - light in his dam-na - tion! What an awk - ward sit - u-
M.
Tre - ma! tre - ma!
Venge-ance! Venge-ance!
cresc.
f
Donna Anna.
tre - ma, tre - - - - ma,
For your crimes re-
Zerlina.
tre - ma, tre - - - - ma, o
For your crimes re-
Donna Elvira.
tre - ma, tre - ma, tre - ma, tre - ma, o
Jus - tice, jus - tice for the crimes, Of your
Don Octavio.
tre - ma, tre - ma, tre - ma, tre - ma, o
Jus - tice, jus - tice for the crimes, Of your
pe - sta mi - nac - cian - do, o Dio, mi va!
a - tion! How I wish I were in bed!
pe - sta mi - nac - cian - do, o Dio, lo va!
a - tion! How I wish I were in bed!
tre - ma, tre - ma, tre - ma, tre - ma, o
Jus - tice, jus - tice for the crimes, Of your

Donna Anna, Donna Elvira & Zerlina.
scel - le - ra - to! O - di il
venge ap-proach-es! Mark the
scel - le - ra - to!
venge ap-proach-es!
scel - le - ra - to!
life ap-proach-es!
scel - le - ra - to! O - di il
life ap-proach-es! Mark the
È confu - sa la mia te - sta, non sò più quel ch'io mi faccia,
What a tempest! How like fu-ries! They de-light in my dam - na - tion!
È confu - sa la sua te - sta, non sa più quel ch'ei si faccia,
What a tempest! How like fu-ries! They de-light in his dam - na - tion!
sce - le - ra - to! O di il
life ap-proach-es! Mark the
tuon del - la ven - det - ta!
voice of wrath e - ter - nal!
tuon del - la ven - det - ta!
voice of wrath e - ter - nal!
e un or - ri - bi - le tem - pe - sta mi - nacciando, o Dio, mi
What an awk-ward sit - u - a - tion! How I wish I were in
e un or - ri - bi - le tem - pe - sta mi - nacciando, o Dio, lo
What an awk-ward sit - u - a - tion! How I wish I were in
tuon del - la ven - det - ta!
voice of wrath e - ter - nal!

A. E. Z.
O - di il tuon del - la ven - det - ta, che ti fi - schia in - tor - no in -
Mark the voice of wrath e - ter - nal! To our own, ac - cord is
O.
O - di il tuon del - la ven - det - ta, che ti fi - schia in - tor - no in -
Mark the voice of wrath e - ter - nal! To our own, ac - cord is
G.
va!
bed!
L.
va!
bed!
M.
O - di il tuon del - la ven - det - ta, che ti fi - schia in - tor - no in -
Mark the voice of wrath e - ter - nal! To our own, ac - cord is
tr
A. E. Z.
tor - no, sul tuo ca - po in que - sto gior - no il suo ful - mi - ne ca -
giv - en: Mor - tal venge - ance armed by Heav - en Soon must fall up - on your
O.
tor - no, sul tuo ca - po in que - sto gior - no il suo ful - mi - ne ca -
giv - en: Mor - tal venge - ance armed by Heav - en Soon must fall up - on your
Masetto.
M.
tor - no, sul tuo ca - po in que - sto gior - no il suo ful - mi - ne ca -
giv - en: Mor - tal venge - ance armed by Heav - en Soon must fall up - on your
A. E. Z.
drà, sì, ca - drà, il suo ful - mi - ne ca - drà!
head! Soon must fall, Soon must fall up - on your head!
O.
drà, sì, ca - drà, il suo ful - mi - ne ca - drà!
head! Soon must fall, Soon must fall up - on your head!
Don Giovanni.
M. G.
drà, sì, ca - drà, il suo ful - mi - ne ca - drà! Ma non
head! Soon must fall, Soon must fall up - on your head! Though you
Vln
p

A. F. Z.
O - di il tuon!
Mark the voice!
O.
O - di il tuon!
Mark the voice!
G.
man - ca in me co - rag - gio,
arm your rage with light-ning . . .
non mi
Cry your
Leporello.
L.
Ma non manca in lui co-rag-gio,
Nev-er will his cour-age fail him . . .
Masetto.
M.
O - di il tuon!
Mark the voice!
f
p
più stretto
A. F. Z.
O - di il tuon!
Mark the voice!
O.
O - di il tuon!
Mark the voice!
G.
per - do, o mi con - fon - do.
venge - ance in the thun - der . . .
Se ca -
Yet I
L.
non si per-de o si con-fon - de.
Cry your venge-ance in the thun-der . . .
Se ca -
Yet he
M.
O - di il tuon!
Mark the voice!
f
ff più stretto
Bassi

A.
F.
Z.
Sul tuo ca-po in que-sto gior-no il suo ful-mi-ne cadrà, il suo ful-mi-
Mor - tal venge-ance armed by Heav-en Soon will fall up-on your head, Soon will fall up-
O.
Sul tuo ca - po in que-sto gior - no il suo ful-mi-
Mor-tal venge - ance is armed by Heav - en Soon to fall up-
G.
des-se an-co-ra il mon-do, ca-desse an-co-ra il mon-do, nul-la mai te-mer, te-
will not shrink in won-der, I will not shrink in won-der Nor be taught Re-gret, re-
L.
des-se an-co-ra il mon-do, ca-desse an-co-ra il mon-do, nul-la mai te-mer, te-
will not shrink in won-der, he will not shrink in won-der Nor be taught Re-gret, re-
M.
Sul tuo ca - po in que-sto gior - no il suo ful-mi-
Mor-tal venge - ance is armed by Heav - en Soon to fall up-
ne ca - drà, sul tuo ca-po in que-sto gior-no, il suo ful-mi-ne ca-
on your head! Mor - tal venge-ance armed by Heav-en Soon will fall up-on your
ne ca - drà, sul tuo ca - po, in que-sto gior - no,
on your head! Mor-tal venge - ance is armed by Heav - en
mer mi fa, se ca-desse an-cora il mon-do, se ca-desse an-co-ra il mon-do,
morse or dread! Nev - er will I shrink in won-der, I will not shrink in won-der
mer lo fa, se ca-desse an-cora il mon-do, se ca-desse an-co-ra il mon-do,
morse or dread! Nev - er will he shrink in won-der, he will not shrink in won-der
ne ca - drà, sul tuo ca - po, in que-sto gior - no,
on your head! Mor-tal venge - ance is armed by Heav - en

A. E. Z.
drà, il suo ful-mi-ne ca-drà, il suo ful-mi-ne ca-drà, il suo
head, Soon will fall up-on your head! The re-venge of man and God Soon will
O.
il suo ful-mi-ne ca-drà, il suo ful-mi-ne ca-drà, il suo
Soon to fall up-on your head! The re-venge of man and God Soon will
G.
nul-la mai te-mer, te-mer mi fa, nul-la mai te-mer mi fa, nul-la
Nor be taught Re-gret, re-morse or dread, Nor be taught re-morse or dread, Nor be
L.
nul-la mai te-mer, te-mer lo fa, nul-la mai te-mer lo fa, nul-la
Nor be taught Re-gret, re-morse or dread, Nor be taught re-morse or dread, Nor be
M.
il suo ful-mi-ne ca-drà, il suo ful-mi-ne ca-drà, il suo
Soon to fall up-on your head! The re-venge of man and God Soon will
A. E. Z.
ful-mi-ne ca-drà, il suo ful-mi-ne ca-drà!
fall up-on your head, Soon will fall up-on your head!
O.
ful-mi-ne ca-drà, il suo ful-mi-ne ca-drà!
fall up-on your head, Soon will fall up-on your head!
(Don Giovanni, seizing Leporello by the collar, and pushing him on before, makes his way through the peasants pressing upon him, and exit.)
G.
mai te-mer mi fa, nul-la mai te-mer mi fa!
taught re-morse or dread, Nor be taught re-morse or dread!
L.
mai te-mer lo fa, nul-la mai te-mer lo fa!
taught re-morse or dread, Nor be taught re-morse or dread!
M.
ful-mi-ne ca-drà, il suo ful-mi-ne ca-drà!
fall up-on your head, Soon will fall up-on your head!
End of Act I

Act II.

Nº 14. "Eh via, buffone, eh via.,,

Duet.

Scene.— A Street.

G.
L.
Eh via, buf -
Come, you big
bur - lo, ed io non bur-lo, bur-lo, bur - lo, ma vo-glio an - dar!
tell you your fun-ny lit - tle, fun-ny lit - tle joke went too far.
tr
cresc.
f p
fp
fo - ne, sen - ti-mi a - mi - co; va che sei mat-to, va che sei
boo - by, sol - emn ex - pres - sions do not be-come you. You're being
No, no, pa - dro - ne! vo' an - dar, vi di - co, No,
I can see noth - ing, noth - ing to laugh at. Joke!
f. p
fp
mat - to, va che sei mat-to, va che sei mat - to, mat-to, mat-to, matto!
sil - ly, you're be-ing sil - ly, you're be-ing ver - y, ver - y, ver - y sil-ly!
no, no, no, no,no,no,no,no,
Joke! Joke! Joke! No,no,no,no,no,
cresc.
f
p
Va che sei mat - to, va che sei
You're be-ing sil - ly, you're be-ing
no,no,no,no,no,no, non vo' re - star, no, non vo' re - star, sì,
no,no,no,no,no,no, Like it I don't and stay here I won't. No,
cresc.
f
p

G.
mat-to, va che sei mat-to, va che sei mat-to, mat-to, mat-to, mat-to!
sil-ly, you're be-ing sil-ly, you're be-ing ver-y, ver-y, ver-y sil-ly!
L.
sì, sì, sì, sì, sì, sì, sì, sì,
no, no, no, no, no, no, no, no,
cresc.
f
p
G.
Eh via, buf-
Grum-ble a-
L.
sì, sì, sì, sì, sì, sì, sì, voglio an-dar, sì, sì, voglio an-dar! no, no, pa-
no, no, no, no, no, no, Like it I don't and stay here I won't. And don't im-
cresc.
f
tr
p
G.
fo-ne, buf-fo-ne, non mi sec-car. Va che sei mat-to, va che sei
way, then! A-buse me! Heed you I don't. And don't im-ag-ine that you'll im-
L.
dro-ne, no, no, pa-dro-ne, non vo' re-star! ed io non bur-lo, ed io non
ag-ine that you a-muse me, Be-cause you don't. And don't im-ag-ine that you a-
cresc.
p
cresc.
G.
matto, fu per bur-lar, fu per bur-lar, fu per bur-lar, fu per bur-lar!
press me, Because you won't. Grum-ble a-way, grum-ble a-way, Heed you I don't.
L.
burlo, ma voglio andar, ma voglio an-dar, ma voglio an-dar, ma voglio an-dar!
muse me, Because you don't, because you don't, because you don't, be-cause you don't.
p
sf
sf
sf
(Lep. tries to go, Don Giovanni detains him.)

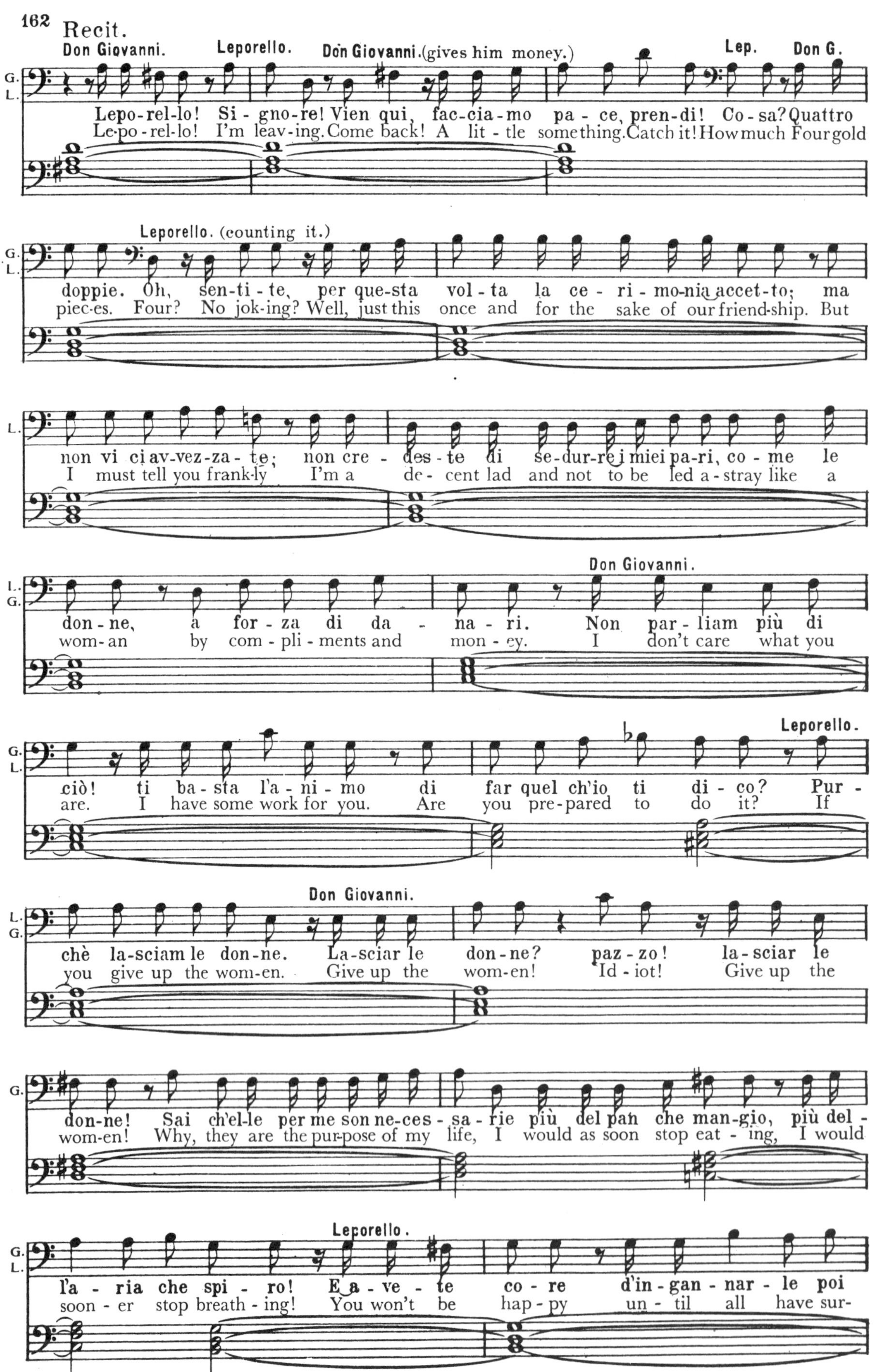
Recit.
Don Giovanni. Leporello. Don Giovanni. (gives him money.) Lep. Don G.
G.
L.
Lepo-rel-lo! Si - gno-re! Vien qui, fac-cia-mo pa - ce, pren-di! Co - sa? Quattro
Le-po - rel-lo! I'm leav-ing. Come back! A lit - tle something. Catch it! How much Four gold
Leporello. (counting it.)
doppie. Oh, sen-ti - te, per que-sta vol - ta la ce - ri - mo-nia accet-to; ma
piec-es. Four? No jok-ing? Well, just this once and for the sake of our friend-ship. But
non vi ci av-vez-za - te; non cre - des - te di se-dur-re i miei pa-ri, co - me le
I must tell you frank-ly I'm a de - cent lad and not to be led a - stray like a
don - ne, a for - za di da - na - ri. Non par - liam più di
wom - an by com - pli - ments and mon - ey. I don't care what you
Don Giovanni.
ciò! ti ba - sta l'a - ni - mo di far quel ch'io ti di - co? Pur -
are. I have some work for you. Are you pre-pared to do it? If
Leporello.
chè la-sciam le don-ne. La-sciar le don - ne? paz - zo! la - sciar le
you give up the wom-en. Give up the wom-en! Id - iot! Give up the
Don Giovanni.
don-ne! Sai ch'el-le per me son ne-ces - sa - rie più del pan che man-gio, più del -
wom-en! Why, they are the pur-pose of my life, I would as soon stop eat - ing, I would
l'a - ria che spi - ro! E a - ve - te co - re d'in - gan - nar - le poi
soon - er stop breath - ing! You won't be hap - py un - til all have sur-
Leporello.

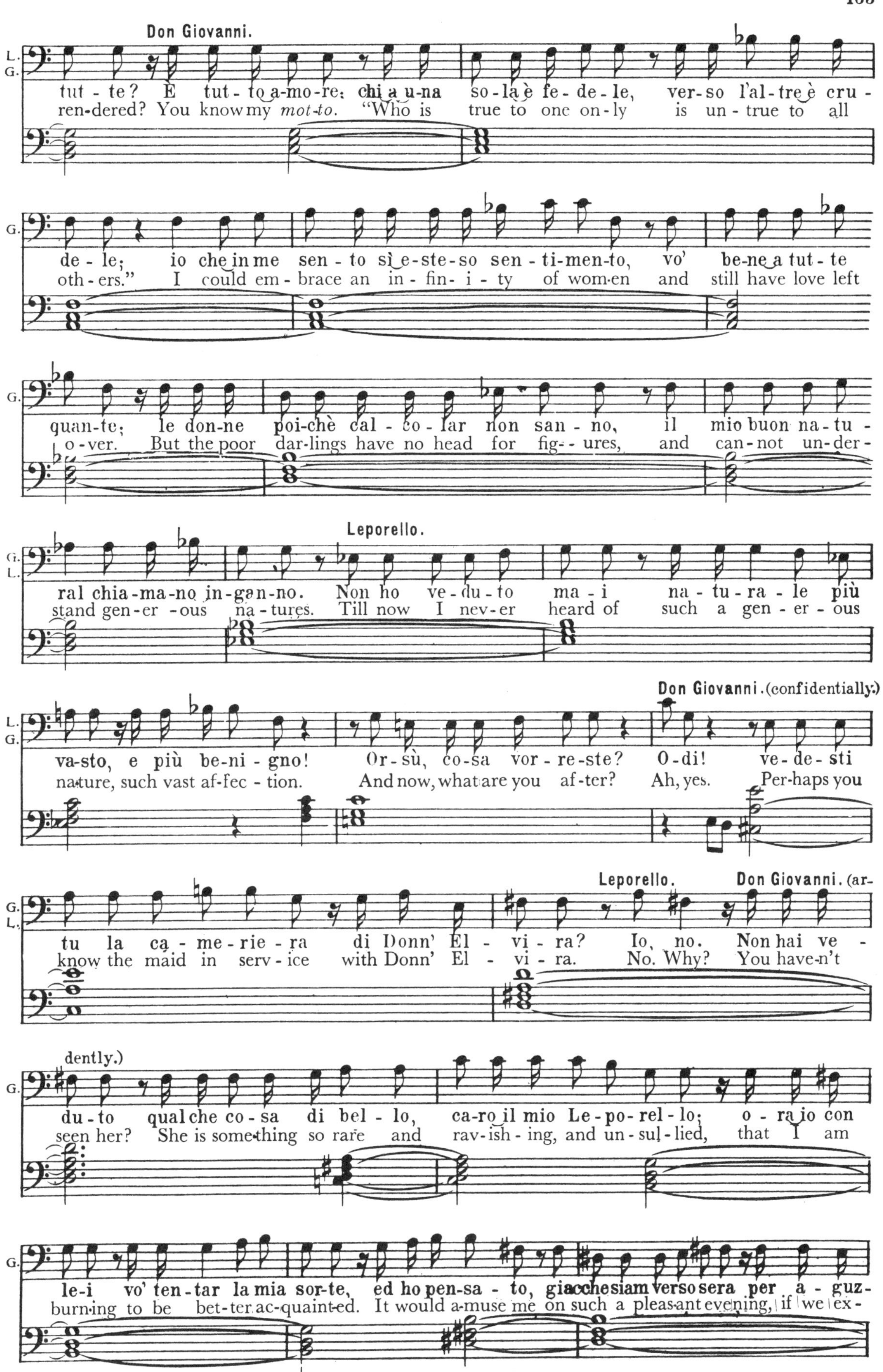
Don Giovanni.
L.
G.
tut - te? È tut - to a-mo-re: chi a u-na so-la è fe-de-le, ver-so l'al-tre è cru -
ren-dered? You know my mot-to. "Who is true to one on-ly is un - true to all
G.
de - le; io che in me sen - to sì e-ste-so sen - ti-men-to, vo' be-ne a tut - te
oth - ers." I could em - brace an in - fin - i - ty of wom-en and still have love left
G.
quan - te; le don-ne poi-chè cal - co - lar non san - no, il mio buon na - tu -
o - ver. But the poor dar-lings have no head for fig - - ures, and can - not un - der -
Leporello.
G.
L.
ral chia-ma-no in-gan-no. Non ho ve - du - to ma - i na - tu - ra - le più
stand gen - er - ous na - tures. Till now I nev - er heard of such a gen - er - ous
Don Giovanni. (confidentially.)
L.
G.
va-sto, e più be-ni - gno! Or-sù, co-sa vor - re-ste? O-di! ve-de-sti
na-ture, such vast af-fec - tion. And now, what are you af - ter? Ah, yes. Per-haps you
Leporello. Don Giovanni. (ar-dently.)
G.
L.
tu la ca - me - rie - ra di Donn' El - vi - ra? Io, no. Non hai ve -
know the maid in serv - ice with Donn' El - vi - ra. No. Why? You have-n't
G.
du - to qual che co - sa di bel - lo, ca-ro il mio Le - po - rel - lo; o - ra io con
seen her? She is some-thing so rare and rav - ish - ing, and un - sul - lied, that I am
G.
le - i vo' ten - tar la mia sor - te, ed ho pen - sa - to, giacchè siam verso sera per a - guz -
burn-ing to be bet - ter ac-quaint-ed. It would a-muse me on such a pleas-ant eve-ning, if we ex -

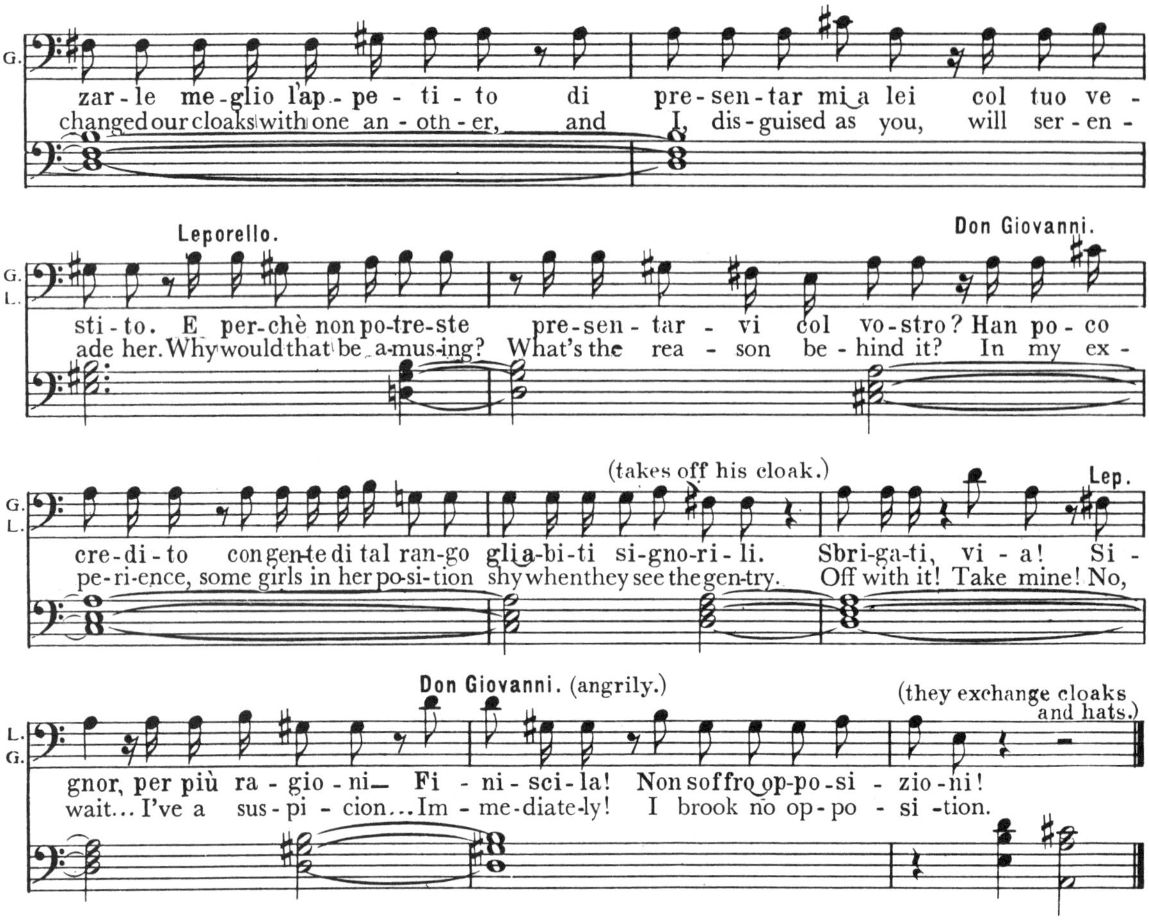

G.
zar-le me-glio l'ap-pe-ti-to di pre-sen-tar mi_a lei col tuo ve-
changed our cloaks with one an-oth-er, and I, dis-guised as you, will ser-en-

Leporello. Don Giovanni.
G. L.
sti-to. E per-chè non po-tre-ste pre-sen-tar-vi col vo-stro? Han po-co
ade her. Why would that be a-mus-ing? What's the rea-son be-hind it? In my ex-

(takes off his cloak.) Lep.
G. L.
cre-di-to con gen-te di tal ran-go gli_a-bi-ti si-gno-ri-li. Sbri-ga-ti, vi-a! Si-
pe-ri-ence, some girls in her po-si-tion shy when they see the gen-try. Off with it! Take mine! No,

Don Giovanni. (angrily.) (they exchange cloaks and hats.)
L. G.
gnor, per più ra-gio-ni- Fi-ni-sci-la! Non soffro op-po-si-zio-ni!
wait... I've a sus-pi-cion... Im-me-diate-ly! I brook no op-po-si-tion.

Nº 15. "Ah, taci, ingiusto core.."

Trio.

Donna Elvira. (at the window.) **Don Giovanni. Leporello.** (It gradually becomes dark.)

empio, è un tra - di - to - re, è col - pa a - ver pie -
did not, he does not love me, Nor shall his love be
Wind & BassVl.
mf
p
tà, è col - pa a - ver pie - tà.
mine, Nor - shall his love be mine.
Leporello. (aside to Don G.)
Zit - to! di Donna El -
Mas - ter, it's Donn'El -
cresc.
Fag.
Bassi & Viola.
Don Giov. (aside to Leporello)
vi - ra, Si - gnor, la vo - ce io sen - to! Co - glie - re io vo'il mo -
vi - ra! You don't want her to find you. I'll hide my - self be -
Fl. Cl.
men - to, tu fer - ma - ti un po' là! tu fer - ma - ti un po'
hind you; My plans are go - ing fine, My plans are go - ing
(stands behind Leporello.)
(making appropriate
là! El - vi - ra, i - do - lo mi - o,
fine. El - vi - ra, hear your lov - er,
tr
Wind.
gestures with Leporello's arms)
El - vi - ra, i - do - lo mi - o!
Your poor re - pent - ant lov - er...
Strs
sf

Donna Elvira.
E.
Non è co-stui l'in-gra-to?
How dare you so ad-dress me?
Don Giovanni.
G.
Sì, vi - ta mi - a, son'
For - give the heart I
mf
p
mf
p
Strings & Cor sustain.
Donna Elvira.
Nu-mi, che strano effet-to
Why should his voice yet stir me?
Don Giovanni.
i - o, e chie-do ca-ri-tà.
of - fer, One weak-ness, on-ly one!
(aside)
Leporello.
L.
Sta-te a ve-der la
She's quite as mad as
Cl.
Fag.
mi si ri-sveglia in pet-to,
Am I, then, doomed for-ev-er?
mi si ri-sve-glia in pet-to!
Am I, then, doomed for-ev-er?
(poking
Di-
O
(crossly, to Don Giovanni)
paz-za,
ev-er!
che ancor gli cre-de-rà, gli cre-de-rà, gli cre-de-rà.
(If I had known your plans, had known your plans, had known your plans!)

Leporello in the ribs, and making more animated gestures)
G.
scen - di, o gio - ja bel - la, o gio - - ja
star, — be not dis - dain - ful, be not — dis -
p
legato
bel - la! ve - drai che tu sei quel - la, che a -
dain - ful, Re - pent - ant love is pain - ful: Your
do - ra l'al - ma mi - - a, pen - ti - to io
faith - ful - ness and beau - - ty Have made me at
Donna Elvira.
E.
No, non ti cre - do, o bar - ba - ro!
No, I can - not be - lieve in you,
so - - - no già! Ah,
heart - con - trite. You
Tutti.
fp
no, non ti credo, o bar - ba - ro! no, non ti credo, o bar - ba - ro!
No, I can - not be - lieve in you, No, I can - not be - lieve in you,
cre - di - mi! ah, cre - di - mi! ah,
must be - lieve, You must be - lieve, You
fp
fp
fp

E.
L.
non ti credo!
No, I cannot!
Leporello. (piano to Don Giovanni.)
Se seguitate, io rido!
I'll die if I don't laugh soon.
G.
credimi! o m'ucci-do! (excitedly, almost in tears.) o m'uc-
must believe, Lest you kill me! I've re-
cresc.
p
mf
ci-do! ah m'ucci-do!
pented. Please have pity!
Leporello.
se seguitate, io rido! se seguitate, io rido, rido, rido,
Unholy titters fill me. She isn't very witty, witty, witty,
un poco cresc.
idolo mio, vien quà!
Come to my arms to-night!
rido, rido, rido, rido, rido, rido, rido!
witty, witty, witty, witty, witty, witty, witty!
Wind
tr
Donna Elvira.
Dei, che cimento è questo!
Shall his avowal sway me?
non sò s'io va-do, o
He makes my heart be-
Spero che cada presto!
Nimbly events obey me,
che bel colpetto è
No human force can
Già quel mendace labbro
If he can still persuade her,
torna a sedur co-
No human force can

E.
G.
L.
re-sto? ah pro - - - teg - ge-te
tray_me. O God, may he be
que-sto? più fer-ti-le ta - len-to del mio no non si
stay_me, The fates were sweet to give me Such tal-ent to de-
ste-i, deh pro - - - teg - ge-te, oh
aid her. May God look af-ter this
sf
mf
p
voi - la mia cre-du - li - tà, cre - du - li -
truth-ful, I want so to be - lieve, want to be-
dà, più fer - ti-le ta - len-to, no, del mio no non si
ceive. The fates were sweet to give me Such a tal - ent to de-
De-i! la sua cre-du - li - tà, cre - du - li -
wom-an, In - cred - i-bly na - ive, much too na-
tà! Dei, che cimen-to è questo, Dei, che cimen-to è questo, non sò s'io
lieve. Should his a-vow-al sway me He makes my heart be-tray me. May he be
dà! Spe-ro che ca-da pre-sto! che bel col-pet-to è
ceive! Nim-bly e-vents o - bey me, No hu-man force can
tà! Già quel menda-ce
ive! If he still can per-
Vl.
Cl.
Fag.

E.
va-do, non sò s'io re-sto! Dei! che ci-men-to è que-sto, non sò s'io va-do, o
truth-ful, may he be truth-ful! Shall his a-vow-al sway me? And make my heart be-
G.
que-sto, che bel col-pet-to, spe-ro che ca-da pre-sto, che bel col-pet-to è
stay me, Nor doubts de-lay me. What cir-cum-stance can stay me? No hu-man force can
L.
labbro torna a se-dur co-ste-i; già quel men-da-ce labbro tor-na a se-dur co-
suade her, No hu-man force can aid her. If he can still per-suade her, What circumstance can
cresc.
f
p
re-sto! Ah pro-teg-ge-te
tray me? O God, may he be
que-sto! più fer-ti-le ta-len-to del mio no non si
stay me, The fates were sweet to give me Such tal-ent to de-
ste-i, deh pro-teg-ge-te oh
aid her? May God pro-tect this
sf
p
mf
mf
p
voi la mia cre-du-li-tà, cre-du-li-tà, la
truth-ful, I want so to be-lieve, I want to be-lieve. I
dà, più fer-ti-le ta-len-to, no del mio, no, non si dà,
ceive. The fates were sweet to give me Such a tal-ent to de-ceive.
De-i, la sua cre-du-li-tà, cre-du-li-tà,
wom-an, In-cred-i-bly na-ive, much too na-ive:
mf
p

(disappears from the window)
E.
mia __ cre - du - li - tà, la mia cre - du - li - tà!
want, __ I _ want to be-lieve. I want, __ I _ want to be-lieve.
G.
no non _ si dà, no non _ si dà!
What art _ is mine when I _ de-ceive!
L.
cre - du - li - tà, cre - du - li - tà!
Her heart and mind are too na-ive!
p
cresc.
p
pp
Recit.
Don Giovanni. (in great spirits.)
Leporello.
Don Giov.
A - mi-co, che ti par? Mi par che abbiate un' a - ni-ma di bronzo. Va
I think the game is mine! You know what I think? I think the game is heartless! Hear!
là, che sei'l gran gonzo! A - scol ta
Hear! An - oth - er ser-mon! You'll still use
(pointing at the window)
be - ne: quan - do co - stei qui vie - ne,
my rules and o - bey my in - struc - tions.
tu cor - ri ad ab-brac-ciar - la, fal - le quat - tro ca - rez - ze, fin - gi la vo - ce
When she comes down, re - mem-ber you're to run and em-brace her, ap - ing my voice and
mi - a: poi con bell' ar - te cer - ca te - co con - dur - la in al - tra
ges - tures. From then on, play your own game just so you go and take her
Leporello.
Don Giovanni.
Leporello.
par - te. Ma, Si - gno - re _ Non più re - pli - che! E se poi mi co - no - sce?
with you. I don't like it. I don't ask you to. But sup - pose she dis - cov - ers?

Don Giovanni.
(softly)
G.
Non ti co - no-sce-rà, se tu non vuo - i; zit-to: ell' a-pre, ehi, giu-di-zio!
If you're in-gen-ious there's no need to wor-ry. Qui-et . . . She's com-ing out. Don't fail me!
He runs off to the side, leaving Leporello alone; Donna Elvira enters from the house, and advances to meet Leporello; Don Giovanni watches their movements from the side.
Donna Elvira. (to Leporello)
Don Giovanni. (aside)
Leporello (aside)
Donna Elvira.
E.
G.
L.
Ec - co mi a vo - i. (Veg-gia-mo che fa - rà.) (Che imbroglio!) Dunque cre-der po -
O my be - lov - ed! (It's much too good to miss.) (It's too much.) Do I dare to be -
E.
trò che i pianti mie-i ab-bian vin - to quel cor? dunque pen-ti - to, l'a-ma-to Don Gio -
lieve my prayers were answered, that you tru - ly re-pent your past be-hav-iour, that you, dear Don Gio -
Leporello.
(imitating D.G's voice.)
Donna Elvira.
E.
L.
vanni, al suo do-ve-re, e all' a-mor mio ri-tor - na? Sì, ca - ri - na! Cru -
van-ni, have owned your er-rors and will no more be faith-less? Yes, be - lieve it. Be -
E.
de - le! se sa - pe - ste quan - te la - gri - me e quan - ti sos-pir voi mi co -
lov - ed, can you real-ize all the a - gon-ies your sud - den de - ser - tion made me
Leporello.
Donna Elvira.
Leporello.
E.
L.
sta - te! Io, vi - ta mi - a? Vo - i. Po - ve - ri - na!
suf - fer? Could I have done it? But now . . . Now, be - lieve me,
Donna Elvira.
Leporello.
Donna Elvira.
L.
E.
quanto mi di-spia-ce! Mi fug - gi - re - te più? No, mu - so bel - lo! Sa - re - te sem-pre
I'm an-oth-er per-son. And you'll al-ways be mine? If you will have me. And you will nev - er
Leporello.
(sighing)
Donna Elvira.
Leporello.
(aside)
E.
L.
mi-o? Sempre! Ca - ris - si - mo! Ca - ris - si - ma! (la bur-la mi dà gu - sto.)
leave me? Leave you? How won-der - ful! A mir - a - cle! (This game is not at all bad!)

Donna Elvira.
Leporello.
Donna Elvira. (embracing him)
Mio te - so - ro! Mia Ve - ne - re! Son per voi tut - ta
How I wait - ed! Pen - el - o - pe! Did you know how I
Leporello.
Don Giovanni.
Donna Elvira.
fo - co. Io tut - to ce - ne - re. (Il bir - bo si ri - scal - da.) E
loved you? I feel I could-n't have! (He may con - vince him - self soon.) And
Leporello.
Donna Elvira.
Leporello.
non m'in - gan - ne - re - te? No, si - cu - ro. Giu - ra - te - mi. Lo
now you know and love me? More each mo - ment! You swear you do? Up-
giu - ro a que - sta ma - no, che ba - cio con tra - spor - to, e a quei bei
on this hand I swear it, and with a kiss con - firm it; up - on this
Donna Elvira.
(escapes with Leporello)
Oh Nu - mi!
A ban - dit!
Don Giovanni. (pretends to waylay them)
Leporello.
D. Giov.
lu - mi. Ih, eh, ah, ah; sei mor - to! Oh Nu - mi! Ih,
fore - arm . . . Stand where you are! De - liv - er! A ban - dit! And
(taking up the
eh, ih, eh, ah, ah! Par che la sor - te mi se - con - di; veg - gia - mo!
that takes care of that! I'm free for more im - por - tant mat - ters. Let's see now . . .
mandolin which Leporello left leaning against the house)
Le fi - ne - stre son que - ste; o - ra can - tia - mo.
for se - duc - ing do - mes - tics, this air works won - ders.

No 16. "Deh vieni alla finestra."
Canzonetta.

G.
rir– vo- gl'i - o!
made– my heart—— thine.
Tu
Be
ch'hai la boc - ca dol - ce più —— che il mie - le,
not — of ad - o - ra - tion dis - tant-ly scorn - ful;
tu che il zuc-che-ro por - ti in mez-zo al co - re!
Grant thy suf-fer-ing sub-ject once more to view —— thee.
Non es-ser, gio - ja mia, con
Des-pon - dent of — thy grace, all
me cru-de - le!
now is mourn - ful,
la-scia-ti al-men ve-der, mio
All —— up-on — thy glance would
bell' — a - mo - re!
Par - ad - ise —— be!

Recit. (Don Giovanni; afterwards Masetto, armed with gun and pistol, and some armed villagers.)
Don Giovanni.
Masetto. (to the peasants.)
G.
M.
Vè gen-te al-la fi-nes-tra: sa-rà des-sa! Zi, zi! Non ci stan-
She's com-ing to the win-dow . . . as they all do. What's that? Keep up your
chia-mo; il cor mi di-ce che tro-var-lo dob-biam. (Qual-cu-no par-la!) Fer-
cour-age, for some-thing tells me that he's not far a-way. (Now who could that be?) Be
Don Giovanni. (aside.)
Masetto.
ma-te-vi; mi pa-re che alcu-no qui si muo-va. (Se non fal-lo, è Ma-set-to!)
vig-il-ant! I think I hear some-bod-y mov-ing. (If it is-n't Ma-set-to!)
Don Giovanni. (folding his cloak closer, and pulling hat over eyes.)
Masetto. (aloud.)
(to the peasants.)
(louder.)
Chi va là? non ri-spon-de; a-ni-mo, schioppo al mu-so! Chi va
Who goes there? Keep to-geth-er! Have your stout wea-pons read-y! Who goes
Don Giovanni. (aside.)
(imitating the voice of Leporello.)
là! (Non è so-lo; ci vuol giu-di-zio.) A-mi-ci! (Non mi
there? (This is awk-ward and calls for cun-ning.) Ma-set-to! (Let us
Masetto. (astonished.)
vo-glio sco-prir.) Sei tu Ma-set-to? Ap-pun-to quel-lo; e
hope that it works!) Is that Ma-set-to? Yes, I'm Ma-set-to. And
Don Giovanni.
Masetto.
tu? Non mi co-no-sci? il ser-vo son io di Don Gio-van-ni. Le-po-
you? Sure-ly you know me. You've of-ten seen me with Don Gio-van-ni. Le-po-
Don Giovanni.
rel-lo! ser-vo di quell' in-de-gno ca-va-lie-re! Cer-to;
rel-lo! You are the man who serves that wick-ed dev-il. Too true!

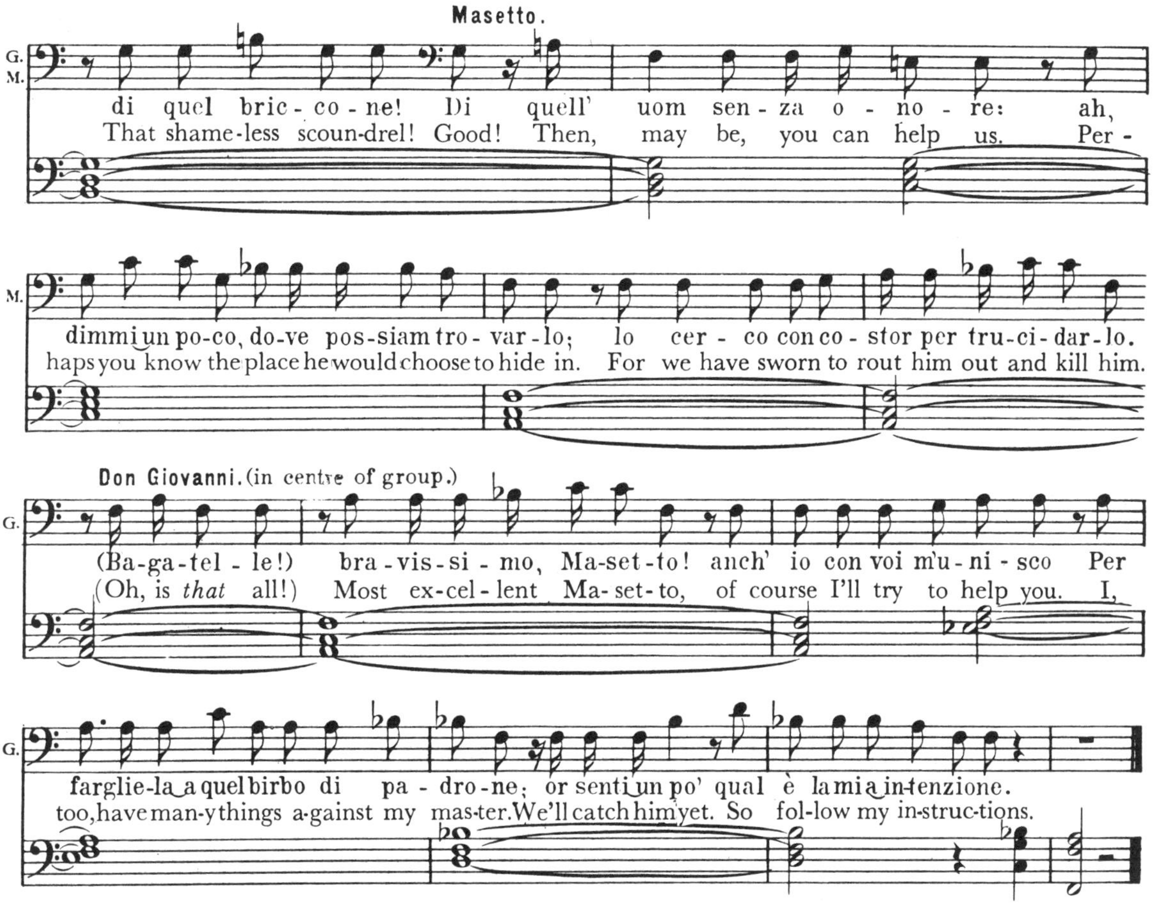

Masetto.

G.
M.

di quel bric-co-ne! Di quell' uom sen-za o-no-re: ah,
That shame-less scoun-drel! Good! Then, may be, you can help us. Per-

M.

dimmi un po-co, do-ve pos-siam tro-var-lo; lo cer-co con co-stor per tru-ci-dar-lo.
haps you know the place he would choose to hide in. For we have sworn to rout him out and kill him.

Don Giovanni. (in centre of group.)

G.

(Ba-ga-tel-le!) bra-vis-si-mo, Ma-set-to! anch' io con voi m'u-ni-sco Per
(Oh, is *that* all!) Most ex-cel-lent Ma-set-to, of course I'll try to help you. I,

G.

farglie-la a quel birbo di pa-dro-ne; or senti un po' qual è la mia in-tenzione.
too, have man-y things a-gainst my mas-ter. We'll catch him yet. So fol-low my in-struc-tions.

Nº 17. "Metà di voi quà vadano."

Aria.

Andante con moto.

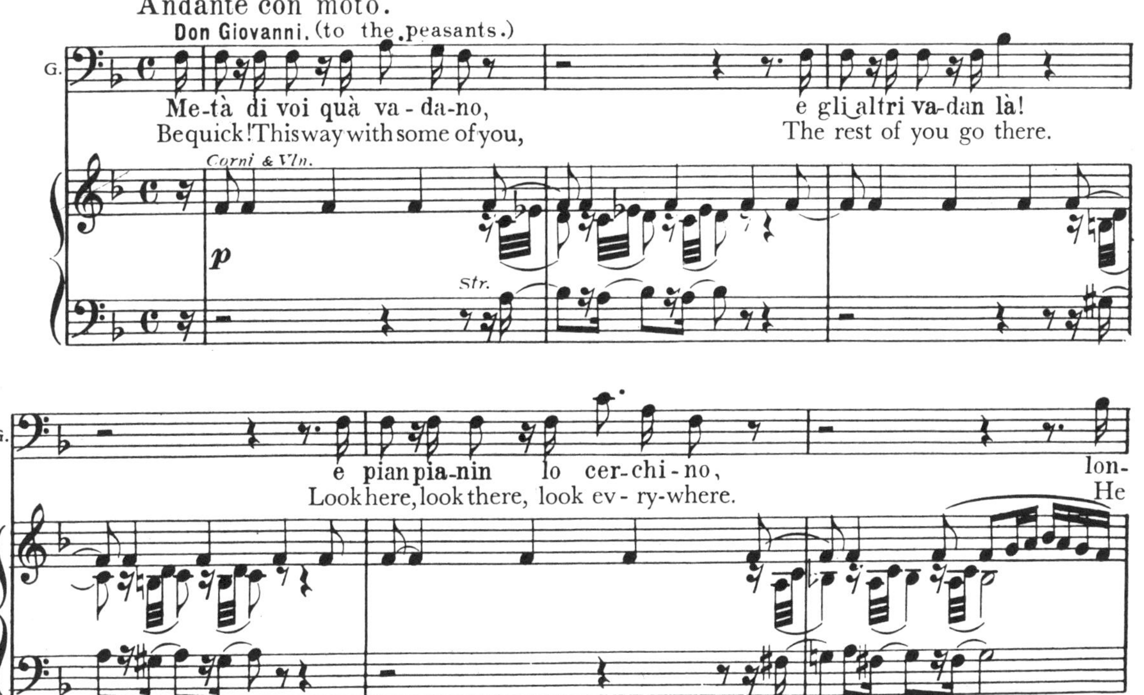

G.
tan non sia di quà, no! lon - tan, lontan non sia di quà.
won't be far a - way. No. Look sharp. He won't be far a - way.
Fl. & Vlns.
p
(going from one to another.)
Se un uom'e una ra - gaz-za pas - seg-gian per la piaz-za, se sot-to a una fi -
Perhaps you'll find him kiss-ing Your sweet-heart in a cor-ner Or soft - ly ser-en -
Fag.
ne-stra fa-re al-l'a-mor sen - ti - te, fe - ri - te pur, fe - ri - te, fe - ri - te pur, fe -
ad - ing Your pret-ty lit-tle daugh-ter. Lay hold of him and bash him. Then knock him down and
Corni sustain.
ri - te, il mio pa-dron sa - rà!
thrash him. He won't be hard to find.
Str.
f
p
In testa egli ha un cap - pel - lo con can-di-di pen -
You'll know him by his swag - ger, His vel-vet cloak and

nac-chi, ad-dos - so un-gran man-tel - lo, e
feath-er: Per-haps I ought to warn you He
cresc.
spa - da al fian - co e-gli ha, e spa - da al fian - co e-
al - so wears a sword, He al - so wears a
(trying to send the peasants off; but they act as if they had not understood him.)
gli ha, e spa - da al fian - co e - gli ha, e spa - da al fian - co e -
sword, He al - so wears a sword, A sharp and shin - ing
cresc.
gli ha, e spa - da al fian - co e - gli ha.
sword, A sharp and shin - ing sword.
(repeating his directions.)
Se un uom' e u - na ra -
So when you've found him
Fag.
gaz - za pas - seg - gian per la piaz - za, Se sot - to a una fi -
kiss - ing Your sweet-heart in a cor - ner, Or soft - ly ser - en -
Str.

G.
ne-stra fare all' a-mor sen-ti-te, fe-ri-te, fe-ri-te, fe-ri-te, pur fe-
ad-ing Your pret-ty lit-tle daugh-ter, Ar-rest him, ar-rest him. Lay hold of him and
Corni sustain.
cresc.
ri-te, fe-ri-te, pur fe-ri-te, fe-ri-te! Me-tà di voi quà va-da-no,
bash him, Then knock him down and thrash him, and bash him. Be quick! This way with some of you,
f
decresc.
Fl. Ob. & Cor. sustain.
e, gli al-tri va-dan là. E
The rest of you go there. Look
pian pianin lo cer-chi-no, lon-tan non sia di
here, look there, look ev-'ry-where. He can't be far a-
(pushing the peasants
quà, no, lon-tan, lon-tan non sia di quà. An-da-te, fa-te
way. No. Look sharp. He can't be far a-way. Don't lose an-oth-er
f
tr
p

off at either side.)

G.

presto, Andate, fate presto, fa - te presto, fate presto fa - te presto, fa - te
moment, be off this very moment, Helter-skelter, helter-skelter, hel - ter-skelter, helter-

tr tr tr tr tr

f p cresc.

(to Masetto.)

G.

presto, Tu sol verrai con me, tu sol verrai con me, verrai con me, verrai con
skelter. But you shall come with me, And I will go with you, will go with you, will go with

Str.

f p cresc. f Tutti.

(putting his arm familiarly around Masetto.)

G.

me, Noi — far dobbiam il re-sto, e già ve-drai cos' è, cos' è, cos'
you. Who'll be the first to spy him? Per-haps it will be me. Who knows? Who

Wood. Str.

sfp p p

G.

è, noi — far dobbiam il re-sto, e già ve-drai cos'
knows? Who'll — be the first to spy him? Per - haps it will be —

sfp

(promenading to and fro with Masetto.)

G.

è, cos' è, cos' è, e già vedrai cos' è, cos' è, cos' è, e già ve-drai cos'
you. Who knows? Who knows? Per-haps it will be me. Who knows? Who knows? Per-haps it will be

(goes off holding Masetto.)
è, e già ve-drai cos' è, e già ve-drai cos' è, e già ve-drai cos' è!
you, Per-haps it will be you, Per-haps it will be me, Per-haps it will be you.
Recit.
(Don Giovanni returns, leading Masetto by the hand.)
Don Giovanni.
Zit-to, la-scia ch'io sen-ta! Ot-ti-ma-men-te: dun-que dob-biam uc-
Qui-et! Halt for a mo-ment! Tell me, Ma-set-to; what do you mean to
Masetto.
Don Giovanni.
ci-der-lo? Si-cu-ro! E non ti ba-ste-ria rom-per-gli l'os-sa, fra-cas-sar-gli le
do to him? To kill him! Sup-pose he got a sound hid-ing to re-mem-ber, would-n't that be suf-
Masetto. (hotly.)
Don Giovanni.
Masetto.
spalle? No, no, voglio ammazzar-lo, vo' far-lo in cento brani. Hai buone ar-mi? Co-
fi-cient? No. No. I want to flay him, to chop him up in piec-es! With what weapon? I'll
(hands musket and pistol to Don Giovanni.)
Don Giovanni.
Masetto.
spetto! ho pria que-sto mo-schet-to, e poi, que-sta pi-sto-la. E po-i? Non
show you. You see I've got this mus-ket, and then I've got a pis-tol. No oth-ers? What

Don Giovanni. (beats him with the flat of his sword.)
M.
G.
ba - sta? Oh, ba-sta certo; or pren-di, que-sta per la pi - sto-la, que-sta per il mo-
oth - ers? Here is your an-swer. Take that now, that for your pret-ty pis-tol, that for your love-ly
Masetto. (crying out and falling.) Don Giovanni.
G.
M.
schetto! Ahi, ahi! la te - sta mi - a! Ta - ci, o sei mor - to! Que - sta per am - maz -
mus-ket! Oh! Oh! My head! I'm — dy-ing. Quiet! Or you will die. That for your thoughts of
(Throws weapons down before Masetto, and exit hastily behind tavern.)
G.
zar-lo, que - sta per far-lo in bra-ni! Vil - la - no, ma-scal - zon! cef - fo da ca-ni!
flay-ing, that for those lit-tle piec-es! You mis - be - got - ten swine, scum of the ditch-es!
Masetto. (crying out.)
Zerlina. (with a lantern.)
M.
Z.
Ahi! ahi! la te - sta mi - a! ahi, ahi, le spal - le, e il pet - to — Di sen-
Oh! Oh! My back is brok-en! Oh God, what bruis - es! I'm dy - ing! Where on
Masetto.
Z.
M.
ti - re mi par - ve la vo - ce di Ma-set-to! O Dio, Zer - li - na, Zer - li - na,
earth did that come from? It sound-ed like Ma-set - to. Oh God! Zer - li - na! Zer - li - na!
Zerlina. Masetto.
M.
Z.
mi - a, soc - cor - so! Co - sa è sta - to? L'i - ni - quo, il scel - le - ra - to mi
Hur-ry! I'm dy-ing! What has hap-pened? That scoun-drel! That ly - ing rob-ber! He's
Zerlina. Masetto.
M.
Z.
rup-pe l'os-sa e i ner-vi. Oh po - ve - ret - ta me! chi? Le - po - rel - lo! o qual-che
crip-pled me for-ev - er! Oh dear, Oh dear, Oh dear! Who? Le - po - rel - lo — or else some
Zerlina. (helping him to rise.)
M.
Z.
dia - vol che so - mi-glia a lu - i! Cru - del! non tel diss' i - o che con que - sto tua
fiend that looked ex-act-ly like him! You see! Ad - mit I told you what would hap - pen if

Z.
paz-za ge-lo-si-a ti ri-dur-re-sti a qual-che brut-to pas-so?
you were al-ways jeal-ous; and now at last it has hap-pened as I told you!
Masetto. Zerlina. Masetto. Zerlina.
Z. M.
do-ve ti duo-le? Qui. E po-i? Qui, e anco-ra qui! E poi non ti duol
Where did he hurt you? Here. Is that all? No it's here and here. No oth-er plac-es
Masetto.
al-tro? Duol-mi un po-co que-sto piè, que-sto brac-cio, e que-sta
hurt you? Well, this foot's a lit-tle sore, and this arm aches, and these two
Zerlina.
M. Z.
ma-no. Via, via, non è gran mal, se il re-sto è sa-no.
fin-gers... Oh well, there's still a lot of you that's health-y.
Vien-te-ne me-co a ca-sa; pur-chè tu mi pro-met-ta d'es-se-re men ge-
Nes-tle a lit-tle closer, and swear to me that you will nev-er-more be sus-
lo-so io, io ti gua-ri rò, ca-ro il mio spo-so.
pi-cious, and I'll ap-ply a salve you'll think de-li-cious.
No. 18. "Vedrai, carino."
Grazioso.
Aria.
Str. Corni sustain.
Mezza voce.
Cello.
tr
Wood.
Zerlina.
Ve-drai, ca-ri-no, se sei buo-ni-no, che bel ri-me-di-o
Nestl-ing se-rene-ly, Warm in my sym-pa-thy, No ach-ing mem-o-ry
p
Cor.

Z.
ti vo-glio dar!
Need you en - dure.
Vl & Wind
tr
È na-tu - ra - le,
Near lies your heal - ing:
Str
non dà di - sgu - sto, e lo spe - zia - le non lo sa far, no,
No un-ap - peal - ing, Un-nat'-ral rem-e-dy. Have I in mind. No.
non lo sa far, no, non lo sa far.
Herbs of some kind? No. Mine is the cure.
È un cer - to bal-sa-mo
It is a hu-man-ly
che por-to ad-dos - so, da - re t'el pos - so, se il vuoi pro - var.
Vir-tu-ous prop-er-ty Heav-en con - fides in me, Want-ing it pure.
Sa-per vor - re - sti
Now shall we prove it?
do - ve mi sta, do - ve, do - ve, do-ve mi sta?
Where can it be? Will you love it, Can I be sure?

(lays Masetto's hand on her heart)
Z.
Fl. Cl. Fag.
Strs. & Corni
Sen - ti - lo bat - te - re,
Here it beats lov - ing - ly.
Toc - ca mi quà, sen - ti - lo
Touch it and see! Here it beats
mf
bat - te - re, sen ti - lo bat - te - re,
lov - ing - ly, Here it beats lov - ing - ly.
toc - ca - mi
Touch it and
p
mf
Vl
Wind
tr
Bassi & Violi
quà! sen - ti - lo bat - te - re, sen - ti - lo bat - te - re,
see! Here it beats lov - ing - ly, Here it beats lov - ing - ly.
sen - ti - lo bat - te - re, toc - ca - mi quà! quà! quà!
Is it not all I swore? Soft - ly it beats, beats, beats.
sen - ti - lo bat - te - re, toc - ca - mi quà, quà! toc - ca - mi quà, quà!
Each throb re - peats to you: I am your com - fort, I am your com - fort,

(Exit with Masetto)
Z.
toc-cami quà, quà, toc-ca-mi quà!
I am your com-fort, And so much more.
cresc.
f
tr
p
pp
Scene. A dark courtyard, with three doors, before the house of Donna Anna. Leporello with Donna Elvira on his arm. He is wearing Don Giovanni's hat and cloak.
Recit. Leporello.
L.
Di mol-te fa-ci il lu-me s'av-vi-ci-na, o mio ben; stia-mo qui a-sco-si,
Dear, I hear peo-ple com-ing. Let us move for a-while in-to the shad-ow
Donna Elvira.
L. E.
fin-chè da noi si sco-sta. Ma che te-mi, a-do-ra-to mio spo-so?
till they have all gone by us. But, my dear-est, what should we be a-fraid of?
Leporello.
(aside)
Nul-la, nul-la cer-ti ri-guar-di, io vo've-der se il lu-me è già lon-ta-no. (Ah
Noth-ing, dar-ling. I was just think-ing per-haps I should find out what they are do-ing. (I
Donna Elvira.
(Leporello goes further away)
co-me da co-stei li-be-rar-mi?) Riman-ti, a-ni-ma bel-la. Ah! non la-sciar-mi!
can-not keep this up for much long-er.) I'll on-ly be a mo-ment. Ah, do not leave me!

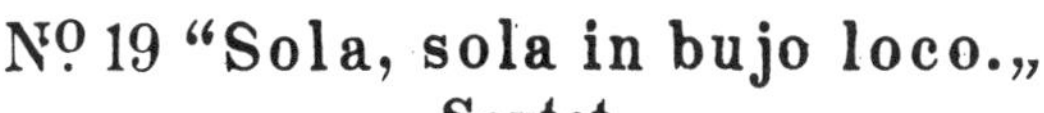

Nº 19 "Sola, sola in bujo loco."

Sextet.

Andante

Donna Elvira.

E.

So-la, so-la in bu-jo lo-co pal-pi-tar il cor mi
Left a-lone, a-lone in dark-ness, all a-lone, I feel up-

p sfp p

Fl. Fag. Strs.

sen-to, e m'as-sa-le un tal spa-ven-to, che mi sem-bra di mo-
on me an op-pres-sion, A chill so dead-ly Fraught with fear and dark with

mf p

Leporello. (groping his way)

rir, che mi sem - - bra di mo-rir. Più che
doom As if waft - - ed from the tomb. It's so

mf p cresc f p Wind

cer-co, men ri-tro-vo que-sta por-ta, ques-ta por-ta scia-gu-ra-ta;
dark here. I can't find it. Lit-tle door, my pret-ty door, where are you hid-ing?

(finds the door) (misses it again)

pia-no, pia-no, l'ho tro-va-ta, l'ho tro-
Here it is, now. No, it is-n't. Ah, I've

Ob

L.
va-ta! ec-co il tem-po di fug-gir, ec-co il tem-po di fug-
found it. Now is the time to dis-ap-pear, Just the mo-ment, just the
(Enter Don
gir, ec-co il tem-po, ec-co il tem-po, ec-co il tem-po di fug-gir!
time, Just the moment, Just the mo-ment, just the time to dis-ap-pear.
Octavio and Donna Anna in mourning)
Don Octavio.
Ter-gi il ci-glio, o vi-ta
Weep no long-er, calm your
Fag. Trombe & Timp.
p
Fl. & Vlns.
mi-a, e dà cal-ma al tuo do-
sor-row, What is done can-not be
Cor. sustain
lo-re! l'om-bra o-
al-tered, An-guish and
mai del ge-ni-to-re pe-na a-
sighs and tears can nev-er Call the
tr

O.
vrà de' tuoi mar tir, de'
dead to life a - gain, to
Donna Anna.
A.
La - scia al - men al - la mia
Leave me, leave me to my
O.
tuoi mar - tir.
life a - gain.
Tympani 2 measures
pe - na que-sto pic - co - lo ri -
sor - row, Noth-ing here on earth can
sto - ro; sol la
please me, Death a - lone can
mor - te, sol la mor - te, o mio te -
ease me, Death a - lone can ease me, Death can

A.
so - ro, il mio piàn - to può fi -
please me, Wipe a - way the guilt - y
nir, il mio pian - - - - to
stain, Dry my tears and
A.
E.
può fi - nir.
ease my pain.
Strs
Donna Elvira. (unseen by the others)
Ah dov' è lo spo - so
Husband, dearest, speak. Where
Leporello. (by the door, unseen by the others)
E.
L.
mi - o? Se mi tro - va, son per -
are you? If I tell her, there'll be
Donna Elvira. (also approaching the door.)
E.
U - na por - ta la vegg' i - o, che - to, che - to io vo' par -
Look, a door al - read - y o - pen. He per - haps has gone that
L.
du - to! U - na por - ta la vegg'
trou - ble. Look, a door al - read - y

E.
tir, che - to, che - to io vo' par - tir!
way. He per-haps has gone that way.
L.
i - o, che - to, che - to io vo' par - tir, che - to, che - to, che - to,
o - pen: Here's my chance to get a - way. Here's my chance to get a -
Wind
Zerlina.
Z.
Fer - ma, bric-co - ne, do - ve ten
Halt! Who are you there? Where are you
Masetto.
M.
Fer - ma, bric-co - ne, do - ve ten
Halt! Who are you there? Where are you
Leporello. (trying to escape, he is suddenly confronted by Zerlina and Masetto.)
L.
che - to, che - to, che - to io vo' par - tir.
way. O Here's my chance to get a - way.
Tutti
Donna Anna. (Leporello, forced into centre, kneels, and hides his face in Don Giovanni's cloak.)
A.
Ec - co il fel - lo - ne, com' e - ra
Ah, now we've got you, brought you to
Zerlina.
Z.
va - i?
off to?
Don Octavio.
O.
Ec - co il fel - lo - ne, com' e - ra
Ah, now we've got you, brought you to
Masetto.
M.
va - i?
off to?

A.
quà? Ah, mo-ra il per - fi - do! che m'ha tra -
bay. He is the mur - der - er! Bring him to
Z.
Ah, mo-ra il per - fi - do! che m'ha tra -
He is the mur - der - er! Bring him to
O.
quà? Ah, mo-ra il per - fi - do! che m'ha tra -
bay. He is the mur - der - er! Bring him to
M.
Ah, mo-ra il per - fi - do! che m'ha tra -
He is the mur - der - er! Bring him to
A.
di - to, che m'ha tra - di - to!
judg - ment! We will have venge-ance!
Z.
di - to, che m'ha tra - di - to!
judg - ment! We will have venge-ance!
O.
di - to, che m'ha tra - di - to!
judg - ment! We will have venge-ance!
M.
di - to, che m'ha tra - di - to!
judg - ment! We will have venge-ance!
Strs.
p
Donna Elvira. (discovering herself, and unveiling)
E.
O mio ma - ri - to! pie - tà, pie-tà, pie -
O spare my hus - band! For - bear. For-bear. For -

Donna Anna.
(sotto voce)
È Donna Elvi-ra? è Don - na El - vi - ra?
It's Donn'El-vi-ra. It's Donn' El - vi - ra.
Donna Elvira.
tà!
bear.
Zerlina.
(sotto voce)
È Donna El-vi-ra? è Donna El-vi - ra?
It's Donn'El - vi-ra. It's Donn'El - vi - ra.
Don Octavio.
(sotto voce)
È Donna Elvi-ra? Donna El-vi - ra?
It's Donn'El - vi-ra! Donn'El-vi - ra!
Masetto.
(sotto voce)
È Donna El-vi - ra?
It's Donn'El - vi - ra.
Donna Anna.
quel - la ch'io ve - do? ap - pe - na il
Would she have par - doned a sin - ner so
Zerlina.
quel - la ch'io ve-do? ap-pe - na il cre - do, ap-pe - na il
Would — she have par-doned a sin - ner so hard-ened, a sin - ner so
Don Octavio.
quel-la ch'io ve - do? ap - pe - na il
Would she have par - doned a sin - ner so
Masetto.
quel - la ch'io ve - do? ap - pe - na il
Would she have par - doned a sin - ner so

A.
E.
Z.
O.
M.
f
cre - do! No, no, no, no! mor-
hard - ened? No, no, no, no! He
Pie - tà, pie - tà,
For - bear. For - bear.
cre - do! No, no, no no! mor-
hard - ened? No, no, no, no! He
cre - do! No, no, no, no! mor-
hard - ened? No, no, no, no! He
cre - do! No, no, no, no! mor-
hard - ened? No, no, no, no! He
Tutti
Vlns
Cor
Bassi
Donna Anna.
rà! No,
dies. No,
Donna Elvira.
Pie - tà! Pie - tà!
Have mer - cy. Have mer - cy.
Zerlina.
rà! No,
dies. No,
Don Octavio.
rà! No,
dies. No,
Masetto.
rà! No,
dies. No,
p
f p

A.
no, no, no, no, no,
no, no, no, no, no.
E.
pie - tà, pie - tà,
For bear. For bear.
Z.
no, no, no, no, no,
no, no, no, no, no.
O.
no, no, no, no, no,
no, no, no, no, no.
M.
no, no, no, no, no,
no, no, no, no, no.
f p f
Donna Anna.
A.
mor - rà!
He dies.
Zerlina.
Z.
mor - rà!
He dies.
(They seize upon him, Leporello discovers himself and kneels down)
Don Octavio.
O.
mor - rà!
He dies.
Masetto.
M.
mor - rà!
He dies.
(as though in tears)
Leporello.
L.
Per - don, per - do - no! Si - gno - ri
No, no, don't hurt me. You are mis -
Fl. Ob. Fag.
fp cresc. p
Leporello.
L.
mie - i! quello io non so - no, sbaglia co -
tak - en. I have done noth - ing, I'm not the
p cresc. p

(Throwing back the cloak. General astonishment; Donna Elvira flies to Donna Anna.)
L.
ste - i, vi - ver la - scia - te - mi per ca - ri -
cul - prit. Sure - ly, you would - n't kill poor lit - tle
cresc.
f
p
tà, vi - ver la - scia - te - mi per ca - ri - tà, per ca - ri -
me. Sure - ly, you would - n't kill poor lit - tle me, poor lit - tle
Donna Anna.
sotto voce
Dei! Le - po - rel - lo? Che in - gan - no è
What! Le - po - rel - lo! I must be
Donna Elvira.
Zerlina.
Don Octavio.
Masetto.
Leporello.
tà, per ca - ri - tà!
me, poor lit - tle me.
tr
A.
E.
Z.
O.
M.

A.
que - sto!
dream-ing,
(p)
Le - - po - rel - lo?
Le - - po - rel - lo!
E.
Z.
O.
M.
p
f
Che ingan-no è que-sto!
I must be dream-ing,
(p)
stu - pi - da re - sto!
stu - pi - do re - sto!
Who would be-lieve it?

A.
che mai sa - rà, che mai sa - rà,
Can this be true? Can this be true?
E.
che mai sa - rà, che mai sa - rà, che mai sa -
Can this be true? Can this be true? Can this be
Z.
che mai sa - rà, che mai sa - rà, che mai sa -
Can this be true? Can this be true? Can this be
O.
che mai sa - rà, che mai sa - rà, che mai sa -
Can this be true? Can this be true? Can this be
M.
che mai sa - rà, che mai sa -
Can this be true? Can this be
A.
che mai sa - rà, che mai sa - rà!
Can this be true? Can this be true?
E.
-rà, che mai sa - rà, che mai sa - rà!
true? Can this be true? Can this be true?
Z.
-rà, che mai sa - rà, che mai sä - rà!
true? Can this be true? Can this be true?
O.
-rà, che mai sa - rà, che mai sa - rà!
true? Can this be true? Can this be true?
M.
-rà, che mai sa - rà, che mai sa - rà!
true? Can this be true? Can this be true?

Molto allegro.
Leporello.
Mil - - le tor - bi - di pen - sie - ri
Fear and ter - ri - ble fore - bod - ing
Donna Anna.
Mil - le tor - bi di pen - sie - ri
Doubt, a - - maze - ment, fear, fore - bod - ing
Donna Elvira.
Mil - le tor - bi - di pen-sie - ri
Doubt, a - - maze - ment, fear, fore-bod-ing
Zerlina.
Mil - le tor - bi - di pen - sie - ri
Doubt, a - - maze - ment, fear, fore - bod-ing
Don Octavio.
Mil - le tor - bi - di pen - sie - ri
Doubt, a - - maze - ment, fear, fore - bod - ing
Masetto.
Mil - le tor - bi - di pen - sie - ri
Doubt, a - - maze - ment, fear, fore - bod - ing
Leporello.
mi s'ag - - gi - ran per la
Leave me shak - en and be -

Donna Anna.
A.
mi s'ag - gi - ran per la te - sta.
Leave me shak - en and be - wild-ered.
Donna Elvira.
E.
mi s'ag - gi - ran per la te - sta.
Leave me shak - en and be - wild-ered.
Zerlina.
Z.
mi s'ag - gi - ran per la te - sta.
Leave me shak - en and be - wild-ered.
Don Octavio.
O.
mi s'ag - gi - ran per la te - sta.
Leave me shak - en and be - wild-ered.
Masetto.
M.
mi s'ag - gi - ran per la te - sta.
Leave me shak - en and be - wild-ered.
Leporello.
L.
te - sta. Mil - le tor - bi - di pen -
wild-ered. Fear and ter - ri - ble fore -
f
p
Leporello.
L.
cresc.
sie - ri mi s'ag-gi - ran per la te - sta; se mi sal - vo in tal tem -
bod - ing Leave me shak - en and be - wild-ered. Will they hang poor Le - po -
cresc.
f
L.
pe - sta, è un pro - di - gio in ve - ri - tà.
rel - lo Who did noth - ing and meant well?
f

A.
Che gior- na - ta, o stel - le, è que-sta, o stel - le, è questa!
Day of won-der! Some rev - el - a - tion is yet to fol-low.
E.
Che gior- na - ta, o stel - le, è que-sta, o stel - le, è questa!
Day of won-der! Some rev - el - a - tion is yet to fol-low.
Z.
Che gior- na - ta, o stel - le, è que-sta, o stel - le, è questa!
Day of won-der! Some rev - el - a - tion, is yet to fol-low.
O.
Che gior- na - ta, o stel - le, è que-sta, o stel - le, è questa!
Day of won-der! Some rev - el - a - tion is yet to fol-low.
M.
Che gior- na - ta, o stel - le, è que-sta, o stel - le, è questa!
Day of won-der! Some rev - el - a - tion is yet to fol-low.
L.
è un pro - di - gio in ve - ri - tà, se mi
Who did noth - ing and meant so well? Will they
sf
sf
Wind.
Str.
L.
sal-vo in tal tem-pe-sta, è un pro-di-gio in ve-ri-tà, è un pro-di-gio in ve-ri-
hang me, poor Le-po - rel-lo, Who did noth-ing and meant so well? Will they hang poor Le-po-
f
L.
tà, in ve-ri-tà, in ve - ri - tà, è un pro - di - gio in ve - ri -
rel-lo Who did noth-ing and meant well, Who did noth-ing and meant so
sf
sf
fp
fp

D. Anna. (sotto voce)
A.
Che im - pen - sa - ta no - vi - tà!
What will fol - low none can tell.
D. Elv.
(sotto voce)
E.
Che im - pen - sa - ta no - vi - tà!
What will fol - low none can tell.
Zerlina.
(sotto voce)
Z.
Che im - pen - sa - ta no - vi - tà!
What will fol - low none can tell.
D. Oct.
O.
(sotto voce)
Che im - pen - sa - ta no - vi - tà!
What will fol - low none can tell.
Mas.
(sotto voce)
M.
Che im - pen - sa - ta no - vi - tà!
What will fol - low none can tell.
Lep.
L.
p
tà! Mil - le tor - bi - di pen - sie - ri mi s'ag -
well? Fear and ter - ri - ble fore - bod - ing Leave me
Vln.
Wind.
Vln.
p
p
che im - pen - sa - ta, che im - pen - sa - ta no - vi -
What will fol - low, What will fol - low none can
che im - pen - sa - ta, che im - pen - sa - ta no - vi -
What will fol - low, What will fol - low none can
che im - pen - sa - ta, che im - pen - sa - ta no - vi -
What will fol - low, What will fol - low none can
che im - pen - sa - ta, che im - pen - sa - ta no - vi -
What will fol - low, What will fol - low none can
che im - pen - sa - ta, che im - pen - sa - ta no - vi -
What will fol - low, What will fol - low none can
gi - ran per la te - sta! se mi sal - vo in tal tempe - sta, è un pro - di - gio
shak - en and be - wild - ered. Will they hang me, poor Le - po - rel - lo, Who did noth - ing

A.
E.
Z.
O.
M.
L.
tà! no - - vi -
tell, none can
tà! che im - pen - sa - ta no - - vi - -
tell. What will fol - low none can
tà! che impen - sa - ta no - vi -
tell. What will fol - low none can
tà! che im - pen - sa - ta no - - vi - -
tell. What will fol - low none can
tà! che im - pen - sa - ta no - - vi - -
tell. What will fol - low none can
in ve - ri - tà! èun pro - di - gio in ve - ri -
and meant so well, Who did nothing and meant so
tà! Mil - le tor - bi - di pen - sie - ri mi s'ag -
tell. Doubt, a - maze-ment, fear, fore - bod-ing Leave me
tà! Mil - le, mil - le tor - bi - di pen - sie - ri
tell. Doubt, a - maze - ment, fear fore - bod - ing Leave me
tà! mil - le tor - bi - di pen - sie - ri
tell. Doubt, a - maze-ment, fear, fore - bod-ing
tà! Mil - le tor - bi - di pen - sie - ri mi s'ag -
tell. Doubt, a - maze-ment, fear, fore - bod-ing Leave me
tà! Mil - le tor - bi - di pen - sie - ri
tell. Doubt, a - maze-ment, fear, fore - bod-ing
tà!
well?

A.
gi - ran per la te - sta.
shak - en and be - wild - ered.
E.
mi s'ag - gi - ran per la
shak - en, shak - en and be -
Z.
mi s'ag - gi - ran per la
Leave me shak - en and be -
O.
gi - ran per la te - sta.
shak - en and be - wild - ered.
M.
mi s'ag - gi - ran per la
Leave me shak - en and be -
E.
te - sta.
wild - ered.
Z.
te - sta.
wild - ered.
M.
te - sta.
wild - ered.
f
Leporello.
L.
cresc.
Mil - le tor - bi - di pen - sie - ri mi s'ag - gi - ran per la
Fear and ter - ri - ble fore - bod - ing Leave me shak - en and be -
p
L.
f
te - sta, se mi sal - vo in tal tem - pe - sta, è un pro - di - gio in ve - ri -
wild - ered. Will they hang poor Le - po - rel - lo Who did noth - ing and meant
cresc.
f

D. Anna.
A.
Che giornata, o stel-le,e
Day of wonder! Some revel-
D. Elvira.
E.
Che giornata, o stel-le,e
Day of wonder! Some revel-
Zerlina.
Z.
Che giornata, o stel-le,e
Day of wonder! Some revel-
D. Octavio.
O.
Che giornata, o stel-le,e
Day of wonder! Some revel-
Masetto.
M.
Che giornata, o stel-le,e
Day of wonder! Some revel-
Leporello.
L.
tà, è,un prodigio
well, Who did nothing
sf
sf
questa, o stel-le,e questa!
ation is yet to follow.
in verità, se mi salvo in tal tem-
and meant so well? Will they hang me, poor Lepo-
Strings
Wind
f

L.
pe-sta è un pro-di-gio in ve-ri-tà, è un pro-di-gio in ve-ri-
rel-lo, Who did noth-ing and meant so well? Will they hang me, poor Le-po-
L.
tà, in ve-ri-tà, in ve-ri-tà, è un pro-di-gio in ve-ri-
rel-lo, Who did nothing and meant so well, Who did noth-ing and meant so
sf
sf
fp
fp
D. Anna.
sotto voce
A.
Che im-pen-sa-ta no-vi-tà!
What will fol-low none can tell.
D. Elvira.
sotto voce
E.
Che im-pen-sa-ta no-vi-tà!
What will fol-low none can tell.
Zerlina.
sotto voce
Z.
Che im-pen-sa-ta no-vi-tà!
What will fol-low none can tell.
D. Octavio.
sotto voce
O.
Che im-pen-sa-ta no-vi-tà!
What will fol-low none can tell.
Masetto.
sotto voce
M.
Che im-pen-sa-ta no-vi-tà!
What will fol-low none can tell.
Leporello.
L.
p
tà! Mil-le tor-bi-di pen-sie-ri mi s'ag-
well? Fear and ter-ri-ble fore-bod-ing Leave me
Vln.
Wind.
Vln.
p
p

A. che im- -pen - sa- - -ta, che im - pen-
What ___ will fol - - - low, What will

E. che im- -pen - sa- - -ta, che im - pen-
What ___ will fol - - - low, What will

Z. che im- -pen - sa- - -ta, che im - pen-
What ___ will fol - - - low, What will

O. che im- -pen - sa- - -ta, che im - pen-
What ___ will fol - - - low, What will

M. che im- -pen - sa- - -ta, che im - pen-
What ___ will fol - - - low, What will

L. gi - ran per la te - sta! se mi sal - vo in tal tem - pe - sta, è un pro-
shak - en and be - wild - ered. Will they hang me, poor Le - po - rel - lo, Who did

A. sa - ta no - vi - tà, ___ no -
fol - low none can tell, ___ none

E. sa - ta no - vi - tà, che im - pen - sa - ta no -
fol - low none can tell. What will - fol - low none

Z. sa - ta no - vi - tà, che impen-
fol - low none can tell. What will

O. sa - ta no - vi - tà, che im - pen - sa - ta no -
fol - low none can tell. What will fol - low none

M. sa - ta no - vi - tà, che im - pen - sa - ta no -
fol - low none can tell. What will fol - low none

L. di - gio in ve - ri - tà! è un pro-
noth - ing and meant so well, meant so

A.
-vi- -tà, che im-pen-sa-ta no-vi-tà,
can tell. What will fol-low none can tell.
F.
vi- -tà, che im-pen-sa- -ta no-
can tell. What will fol-low none
Z.
sa-ta no-vi-tà, che im-pen-sa-ta no-vi-tà, che im-pen-
fol-low none can tell. What will fol-low none can tell. What will
O.
vi- -tà, che im-pen-sa- -ta no-
can tell. What will fol-low none
M.
vi- -tà, che im-pen-sa- -ta no-
can tell. What will fol- -low none
L.
di-gio in ve-ri-tà, è un pro-di- -gio in ve-ri-
well, and meant so well, Who did noth-ing and meant so
A.
che im-pen-sa- -ta no- -vi- -tà,
What will fol-low none can tell.
F.
vi- -ta, no- -vi- -tà,
can tell, none can tell.
Z.
sa-ta no- -vi- -tà,
fol-low none can tell.
O.
vi-tà, no- vi- -tà,
can tell, none can tell.
M.
vi- -tà, no- -vi- -tà,
can tell, none can tell.
L.
tà, in ve- -ri- -tà,
well, Who meant so well?
staccato

A.
che im-pen - sa - ta no - vi - tà, che im - pen - sa - ta
What will fol - low none can tell. What will fol - low
F.
che im-pen - sa - ta no - vi - tà, che im-pen - sa - ta
What will fol - low none can tell. What will fol - low
Z.
che im-pen - sa - ta no - vi - tà, che im-pen - sa - ta
What will fol - low none can tell. What will fol - low
O.
che im-pen - sa - ta no - vi - tà, che im-pen - sa - ta
What will fol - low none can tell. What will fol - low
M.
che im-pen - sa - ta no - vi - tà, che im-pen - sa - ta
What will fol - low none can tell What will fol - low
L.
è un pro - di - gio in ve - ri - tà, è un pro - di - gio in
I did noth - ing and meant well I did noth - ing
A.
no - vi - tà, che im-pen - sa - ta, che im - pen - sa -
none can tell. What will fol - low, What will fol -
F.
no - vi - tà, che im-pen - sa - ta, che im - pen - sa -
none can tell. What will fol - low, What will fol -
Z.
no - vi - tà, che im-pen - sa - ta, che im-pen - sa -
none can tell. What will fol - low, What will fol -
O.
no - vi - tà, che im-pen - sa - ta, che im-
none can tell. What will fol - low, What
M.
no - vi - tà, che im-pen - sa - ta,
none can tell. What will fol - low,
L.
ve - ri - tà, è un pro - di - gio
and meant well I did noth - ing

A.
- - - ta no- - - vi - tà, che im - pen -
- - - low none can tell. What will
E.
- - - - - ta no - vi - tà, che im - pen -
- - - - - low none can tell. What will
Z.
- ta no- - - - vi- - tà, che im - pen -
- low none can tell. What will
O.
- pen - sa- - ta no- - vi- - tà, che im - pen -
will fol - - low none can tell. What will
M.
p
che im - pen - sa - ta no - vi - tà, che im - pen -
What will fol - low none can tell. What will
L.
f
È un pro - di- - - -
I did noth - - -
f
f
A.
sa- - ta no- - vi - tà, che im - pen - sa - - ta
fol - low none can tell. What will fol - - low
E.
sa- - ta no- - vi - tà, che im - pen - sa - - ta
fol - - low none can tell. What will fol - - low
Z.
sa- - ta no- - vi - tà, che im - pen - sa - - ta
fol - - low none can tell. What will fol - - low
O.
sa- - ta no- - vi - tà, che im - pen - sa - - ta
fol - - low none can tell. What will fol - - low
M.
sa - ta no - vi - tà, che im - pen - sa - ta
fol - low none can tell. What will fol - low
L.
- gio in ve - ri - tà, è un pro - di- - - gio in
- ing and meant so well. I did noth - - ing and
3
3
3
3

A.
no- -vi - tà, che im - pen - sa - ta no- -vi -
none can tell. What will fol - low none can
E.
no- -vi - tà, che im - pen - sa- -ta no- -vi -
none can tell. What will fol - low none can
Z.
no- -vi - tà, che im - pen - sa- -ta no- -vi -
none can tell. What will fol - low none can
O.
no- -vi - tà, che im - pen - sa- -ta no- -vi -
none can tell. What will fol - low none can
M.
no - vi - tà, che im - pen - sa- -ta no- -vi -
none can tell. What will fol - low none can
L.
ve - ri - tà, è un pro - di- - -gio in ve- -ri -
meant so well. I did noth - - - ing and meant so
(exit D. Anna)
tà!
tell.
tà!
tell.
tà!
tell.
tà!
tell.
tà!
tell.
tà!
well.

Recit.
Zerlina.(to Leporello)
Z.
Dun-que quel-lo sei tu, che il mio Ma-set-to po-co fà cru-del-men-te mal-trat-
It was you, it was you, you sav-age brute, who with your blows ver-y near-ly killed Ma-
Donna Elvira (to Leporello)
Z.
E.
ta-sti! Dun-que tu m'in-gan-na-sti, o scel-le-ra-to, spac-
set-to. It was you, vul-gar scoun-drel, who de-ceived me, be-
Don Octavio.(to Leporello)
E.
O.
cian-do-ti con me da Don Gio-van-ni! Dun-que tu in que-sti pan-ni
hav-ing as if you were Don Gio-van-ni. Dressed to look like his mas-ter.
Donna Elvira.
O.
E.
ve-ni-sti qui per qual-che tra-di-men-to! A me toc-ca pu-
That clear-ly speaks of some ne-far-ious pur-pose. Let me do the chas-
Zerlina. Don Octavio. Masetto.
E.
Z.
O.
M.
nir-lo. An-zi a me. No, no, a me. Ac-cop-pa-te-lo me-co tut-ti tre.
tis-ing. No, let me. No, no, let me. Let us all in a bod-y deal with him.
Allegro assai. Nº 20. "Ah, pietà! Signori miei!,,
Aria.
Leporello.
L.
Ah, pie-tà! Si-gno-ri miei! ah pie-tà, pie-tà, pie-
Ah don't kill me on the spot. Spare my life and I will
fp
fp
L.
tà, pie-tà di me, pie-tà Dò ra-gio-ne a voi, a
tell you what was what, what's what. I'll ex-plain to you and
f p f p

L.

le - i, a voi, a le - i. Ma, ma, il de - lit - to, il de -
you and you and you, But . . . but . . . but the sin - ner, But the

Cor. Fag. & Bassi.

L.

lit - to mio non è, mio non è, Il pa - dron con pre - po -
guilt - y one I'm not, I am not. If you on - ly knew my

Fl.

Str.

L.

ten - za, l'in - no - cen - za mi ru - bò, l'in - no - cen - za mi ru -
mas - ter, You would pit - y me a lot, You would pit - y me a

(to Elvira)

L.

bò. Donna Elvi - ra! compa - ti - te!
lot. Donn'El vi - ra! You can help me.

L.

com - pa - ti - te! Voi ca - pi - te come an -
Won't you help me? You know what he made me

Vlns.

(to Masetto)
L.
dò, voi ca-pi-te, voi ca-pi-te, voi ca-pi-te come an-dò! Di Ma-
do. Please for give me, please for give me For the things he made me do. Of Ma-
Tutti.
(motioning to Elvira)
set-to non sò nul-la, non sò nul-la, nul-la, nul-la, nul-la, nul-la, vel di-
set-to I know noth-ing, I know noth-ing, noth-ing, noth-ing, noth-ing, noth-ing. O most
f
p
rà que-sta fan-ciul-la, que-sta fan-ciul-la. E un o-ret-ta
no-ble gra-cious la-dy, tell them this sto-ry. For the past hour,
tr
fp
cir-cum-cir-ca, che con lei gi-ran-do vo,
per-haps long-er, Where was I? I was with you.
fp
(With embarrassment to Don Octavio)
che con lei gi-ran-do vo. A voi, Si-gnore!
Where was I? I was with you. To you, your lordship,

L.
non di - co nien - te, cer - to ti - mo - re,
how shall I put it? I saw a sort of . . .
certo acci - den - te, di fuo - ri chiaro, di dentro o - scu-ro, non c'è ri-
A sort of wall, you see. A sort of door, you see, And then I thought, you see, It must lead
pa - ro la porta, il mu-ro, io me - ne vo da quel
some where, Well, some how, well, some how, At first I was on the
(pointing at the door)
la - to, poi qui ce - la - to,
out - side . . . Then on the in - side . . .
(slyly edging towards the door)
l'af - far si sa, oh, si
The rest you know. Now you
mf
p
f
sf
tr

L.
sa! ma
know. Were
p
(making for the door)
s'io sa-pe-va, fug-gia per quà, fug-gia per quà, fug-gia per
I a li-ar You see, I'd go, You see, I'd go, You see, I'd
pp mf p mf p
(Runs out.)
quà, fug-gia per quà!
go, You'd see me go.
mf p mf mf mf mf
Recit.
Donna Elvira.
Masetto.
Zerlina.
E. M. Z.
Fer-ma, per-fi-do, fer-ma! Il bir-bo ha l'a-li ai pie-di! Con quel ar-te
Catch him! Af-ter him! Stop him! No hare could fly much fast-er. O how sly-ly
Don Octavio.
Z. O.
si sot-tras-se l'i-ni-quo. A-mi-ci mi-ei, do-po ec-ces-si si e-
he al-layed our sus-pi-cions! From all we've wit-nessed and from what he has
O.
normi, du-bi-tar non pos-siam che Don Gio-van-ni non sia l'em-pio uc-ci-
told us, it is on-ly too clear who did the mur-der. It was Don Gio-

so - re del pa - dre di Donn' An - na; in que - sta ca - sa per po -
van - ni who killed Donn' An - na's fath - er. So I will ask you all to

che o - re ferma - te - vi, un ri - cor - sa vo' far a chi si de - ve, è in poch' i -
stay and look af - ter her while I lay all the facts be - fore the judg - es. Then, ver - y

(Exeunt D. Elvira, Zerlina, and Masetto.)

stanti ven - di - car - vi pro - met - to. Co - sì vuo - le do - ver, pie - ta - de, af - fet - to.
short - ly, re - tri - bu - tion shall fol - low. Let our strength be in love and friendship and hon - or!

No. 21. "Il mio tesoro intanto."

Aria.

Andante grazioso.

Clar. Fag. and Vln.

Strings con sordini, Bassi pizz.

f

Don Octavio.

Il mio te - so - ro in - tan - to an -
Fly, gen - tle notes, to aid her, Sweet

Cl. Fag. *Strings.* *p*

da - te, an - da - - te a con - so - lar! e del bel ci - glio il
mu - sic, as my her - ald, swift - ly fly! Go to my love, per -

Corni sustain.

pian - to cer - ca - te di a - sciu - gar, cer - ca - te, cer - ca - te, cer -
suade her Those flow - ing tears to dry. Sweet mu - sic, at - tend her Of

O.
ca- -te- di a- -sciu-gar, cer-ca-
whom your grace is born: Con-sole
-te di a- -sciu-gar.
her, fly, O fly!
Vln.
Di-te-le,che i suoi tor-ti a ven-di-car io va-do, a
Say she is not for-sak-en, Ev-er shall I de-fend her, E-
vendi-car io va-do. Che sol di stra-gi e mor-ti
ven till death de-fend her, My sol-emn vow is tak-en,
nun-zio vogl'io tor-nar, nun- -zio vogl'io tor-
Nev-er to be for-sworn: Soon shall her wrong-er
f senza sordini
p
cresc.
f
fp
p

nar, sì, nun-zio vogl'io_ tor - nar!
die, soon, soon shall her wrong-er - die.

cresc. f p

Il mio te-so-ro in-
Fly, gen-tle notes, to

con sordini.

tan - to An - da - te, an - da - te a con - so -
aid her, Sweet mu - sic, as my her-ald, swift-ly

lar! e del bel ciglio il pian - to cer - ca - te di a - sciu - gar, cer -
fly! Go to my love, per - suade her Those flow - ing tears to dry. Sweet

ca - te, cer - ca - te, cer - ca - te di a - sciu - gar, cer -
mu - sic, at - tend her Of whom your grace is born: Con -

ca - - - - - - - - - - te
sole her,
tr
dia - sciu-gar. Di - te - le che i suoi tor - ti
fly, O fly! Say she is not for-sak - en,
senza sord.
f
p
f
p
a ven-di-car io va - do, a ven-di-car io
Ev - er-shall I de-fend her, E - ven till death de-
cresc.
va - - - - - - - do, che sol di stra - gi e
fend her, My sol - emn vow is
f
fp
p
mor - ti nun - zio vogl'io tor - nar,
tak - en, Nev - er to be for - sworn:
fp
fp
fp
f
p
f
p

O.
nunzio, nunzio vogl' io tor-
Soon shall, soon shall her wrong - - er
nar, Che sol di stra-gi e mor- ti
die. My sol-emn vow is tak - en,
f
f
p
nun-zio vogl'io tor-nar, sì, nun-zio vogl'io tor-
Nev-er to be for sworn: Soon, soon shall her wrong-er
f
nar!
die. (Exit).
p
tr
f

(Zerlina, with a razor in her hand, drags on Leporello by the hair.)
a tempo
Zerlina.
Re - sta - ti quà! Re - sta - ti quà!
You thought you'd go, you thought me slow.
Leporello.
Per ca - ri - tà!
You're hurt - ing, O!
Zerlina.
Re - sta - ti quà! Re - sta - ti quà, quà,
But now you know it was - n't so. No!
Recit.
Leporello. (trying to free himself).
quà! Per ca - ri - tà, Zer - li - na!
No! You're hurt - ing me, Zer - li - na!
Zerlina.
Eh! non c'è ca - ri - tà per pa - ri
Hurt? That's noth ing to what you're going to
tuo - i.
suf - fer.
Leporello.
Dun - que ca - var - mi vuo - i?
What do you mean? Have pi - ty!
Zerlina.
I ca - pel - li, la te - sta,
First, I'll gouge both your eyes out,
il co - re e gli oc - chi.
then cut out your liv - er.
Leporello. (trying to coax her.)
Sen - ti, ca - ri - na mi - a!
Lis - ten, Dear, sweet Zer - li - na!
Zerlina. (holding him off.)
Guai, se mi toc - chi!
Beast, keep your paws down,
Ve - drai, schiu - ma de' bir - bi, qual pre - mio n'ha chi le ra - gaz - zein -
or I'll make you re - gret it. You must be taught so as you won't for -
giu - ria.
get - it.
Leporello. (aside).
(Li - be - ra - te - mi, o Dei, da que - sta fu - ria!)
O de - liv - er me, dear Heav'n, from this fu - ry!
Zerlina. (dragging Leporello about during the whole scene.)
Ma - set - to! O - là! Ma - set - to! do - ve dia - vo - lo è i - to? Ser - vi!
Ma - set - to! Come here! Ma - set - to! Where on earth has he got to? Come here!

Leporello. (a peasant enters.)
Z.
L.
gen-te! nes-sun vien, nes-sun sen-te Fa pia-no per pie-
Help me! They've all gone, they don't hear me. Don't drag me by the
Zerlina.
tà! non strascinarmi a co-da di ca-val-lo! Ve-drai, vedrai co-me fi-ni-sce il
hair. I'm not a sack of grain that must be cart-ed. You wait and see! I have n't real-ly
Leporello. Zerlina. Leporello.
bal-lo! Pre-sto quà quel-la se-dia! Ec-co-la! Sie-di! Stan-co non
start-ed. Fetch that stool from the cor-ner. Here it is! Sit down! I'd rath-er
Zerlina.
son. Sie-di, o con que-ste ma-ni ti strappo il cor, e poi lo get-to a'
stand. Sit down! Or I'll tear your heart out with this hand. The vil-lage dogs shall
Leporello. (sits down.)
ca-ni. Sie-do, ma tu, di gra-zia, met-ti giù quel ra-so-jo! mi vuoi
eat it. I'll sit. And now, I'm seat-ed. Please don't flour-ish that ra-zor. I've no
Zerlina.
for-se sbar-bar? Sì, ma-scal-zo-ne, io sbar-ba-re ti vo' sen-za sa-
need of a shave. I mean to shave you, and so close-ly your own moth-er won't
Leporello. Zerlina. Leporello. (gives it.)
po-ne. E-ter-ni De-i! Dam-mi la man! La ma-no.
know you. Will no one save me? Give me your hand. With pleas-ure.
Zerlina. Leporello. (gives the others). Zerlina. (ties Leporello's hands with her handkerchief the peasant assists her.)
L'al-tra! Ma che vuoi far-mi? Vog-lio far, vog-lio far quel-lo che par-mi.
The other. What are you up to? You will learn ver-y soon; I'm going to show you.

No. 21b "Per queste tue manine."

Duet.

Allegro moderato.

Z.
L.
nò, nò, pie-tà non v'è!
Could be more fell than I.
Leporello.
Ah, di fug-gir si pro-vi, ah, di fug-gir si pro-vi!
Tell me you're on-ly jok-ing. Tell me you're on-ly jok-ing.
Sei mor - to se ti mo-vi, sei mor-to se ti mo-vi, se ti movi, se ti movi!
If you but move a mus-cle You'll find out who is jok-ing, You will see if I am jok-ing.
p
cresc.
tr
Bar - - ba-ri, ingiu - sti De-i!
Why — don't you catch my mas-ter?
Bar- - ba - ro tra - di - to - re,
Would — I had caught your — mas - ter,
bar - ba - ri, ingiu - sti De-i!
Why don't you catch my mas-ter?
barba-ro tra - di - to - re, del tuo padrone il co-re
Would I had caught your mas-ter! Re-venge would be the sweet-er;
(She ties him to the chair)
a - ves - si qui con
But you will do in -
in ma-no di co - ste - i, chi
Now he will live for - ev - er And

Z.
L.
te, del tuo padrone il co - re a - ves - si qui con te!
stead: Re-venge would be the sweet - er, But you will do in - stead.
ca - pi - tar mi fe', chi ca - pi - tar mi fe'? Deh
I shall soon be dead, And I shall soon be dead. Don't
Sen
Then
non mi stringer tan - to! l'a - ni - ma mia sen va!
draw the knots so tight - ly, Or I shall faint with pain.
va - da, sen va - da, o re - sti, in - tan - to non par - ti - rai di
faint away, Then faint away or bel - low! But here you are go - ing to re -
quà!
main.
Che stret - te, oh Dei, che bot - te! è
She'll carve me in lit - tle slic - es. A
Ob.
tr
sf
p
f

Z.
Di gioja e di di - let - to sen - to brillar mil
No man is to be trust - ed, With smiles they seek to -
L.
gior - no, ovver è not - te? Che
wom - an's heart like ice is. So
Vln.
Fag.
p
tr
pet-to! di gioja e di di - let - to sen - to brillar mil pet-to! co - sì, co-sì cogl'
charm us. No man is to be trust - ed, With smiles they seek to — charm us. The proper way to
scos - se di tre-muoto, che
this is what all wom-en Would
uo - mi-ni, co - sì, co-sì si fa, co - sì, co - sì cogl' uo-mini, co - sì, co-sì si
deal with them, The on - ly way is thus. The prop-er way to deal with them, The on-ly way is
bu - ja o - scu - ri - tà, che bu - ja o - scu - ri -
like to do to us, Would like to do to
fa! Sei mor-to, mor-to, mor-to,
thus. And if you move a mus-cle
tà. Ah! di fug-gir si pro-vi, ah! di fug-gir si provi!
us! Tell me you're on-ly jok-ing. Tell me you're on-ly jok-ing!
cresc.

Z.
L.
mor-to, se ti mo-vi, se ti mo-vi!
You'll find out who's jok-ing, who is jok-ing!
Deh, non mi-strin-ger-tan-to,
Don't draw-the-knots-so-tight-ly
tr
f
sf
p
Wind.
Sen va-da, sen va-da, o re-sti, in-
Then faint a-way, Then faint a-way or bel-low! But
l'a-ni-ma mia sen va!
Or I shall faint with pain.
tan-to non par-ti-rai di quà, non par-ti-rai, non par-ti-rai, non par-ti-rai di
here you are go-ing to re-main, You're go-ing to re-main, You're go-ing safe-ly to re-
cresc.
quà!
main.
Che stret-te, oh Dei! che bot-te! e
She'll carve me in lit-tle slic-es. A
Ob.

Z.
Di gio-ja e di di - let - to sen - to bril - lar mi il
No man is to be trust-ed, With smiles they seek to—
L.
gior - no,ov-ver è not - te? Che
wom - an's heart like ice is. So
Fag.
f
p
tr
Z.
pet-to, di gio-ja e di di - let - to sen - to bril - lar mi il pet-to! co - sì, co - sì, cogl'
charm us.But when they look most kindly,Then most they mean to harm us. The prop-er way to
L.
scos - se di tre - muo-to, che
this is what all wom-en Would
Z.
uo - mi - ni, co - sì, co - sì si fa, co - sì, co - sì, cogl' uo - mi - ni, co - sì, co - sì si
deal with them,The on - ly way is thus, The prop-er way to deal with them,The on - ly way is
L.
bu - ja o - scu - ri - tà, che bu - ja o - scu - ri -
like to do to us, Would like to do to
Z.
fa, co - sì, co - sì, co - sì si fa, co - sì, co - sì, co - sì si
thus,The on - ly, on - ly way is thus, The on - ly, on - ly way is
L.
tà! Oh Dei, che strette! oh Dei, che bot - te!
us! An an - gry wom - an's heart like ice is.
tr

Z.
fa, co - sì, co - sì, co - sì, co - sì, co - sì, co - sì si
thus, The on - ly, on - ly, on - ly, on - ly, on - ly way is

L.
è not-te o gior - no, e gior no o not - te? che
She'll carve me up in lit - tle slic - es. For

Z.
fa, co - sì, co - sì, co - sì, co - sì, co - sì si fa, co - sì, co - sì, co - sì, co -
thus, The on - ly, on - ly, on - ly, on - ly way is thus, The on - ly, on - ly, on - ly,

L.
scos - - - - - - se di
that is what

Z.
sì, co - sì si fa, co - sì. co - sì, co - sì, co - sì si
on - ly way is thus, The on - - ly, on - - ly, on - - ly way is

L.
tre - muo - to, che bu - ja o - scu - ri -
all wom - en Would like to do to

Z.
fa, co-sì, co - sì, co - sì, co - sì si fa, co - sì, co - sì,
thus, The on - ly, on - ly, on - ly way is thus, The on - ly, on -

L.
tà, che bu - ja o - scu - ri - tà, che bu - ja,
us, Would like to do to us, They all would

cresc.

Z. co-sì si — fa!
- ly way is — thus. (exit)

L. bu - ja o - scu - ri - tà!
like to do to us.

Recit.

Leporello. (to the Peasant)

L. A-mi-co, per pie-tà un po-co d'a-qua fres-ca, o ch'io mi
Where are you? Let me go! I want a drink of wa-ter. Don't let me

mo-ro! guar-da un po' co-me stret-to mi le-gò l'as-sas-
die here! Don't leave poor Le-po-rel-lo, All trussed up like a

(Exit Peasant.) (struggling)

si-na! Se po-tes-si li-be-rar-mi coi den-ti? Oh ven-ga il
chick-en. There's no get-ting at these knots to un-tie them. It seems im-

dia-vo-lo a di-sfar que-sti gruppi! io vo' ve-de-re di rom-pe-re la
pos-si-ble, but I won't give up try-ing. There must be some way of break-ing them. I'll

cor-da — co-me è for-te! pau-ra del-la mor-te!
find it. Strong as these cords are, fear of death is strong-er.

(He pulls hard and the window

E tu, Mercu-rio, pro-tet-tor de' la-dri, pro-teg-gi un ga-lant 'uom! co-raggio —
Mer-cu-ry, pa-tron of Light-Fin-gered Serv-ants, though I'm an hon-est lad, as-sist me!

falls to which the end of the cord was fastened.)
L.
bra-vo! pria che co-stei ri - tor - ni, Bi - so-gna dar di spro-ne al-la cal-
Thank you! Could n't you al - so give me a pair of feath-ered san-dals. She must-n't
(Escapes, dragging after him the chair and window.)
L.
ca-gna, E stra-sci - nar, se oc - cor - re, u - na mon - ta - gna!
find me. I'll run and drag if need be a house be - hind me.
Zerlina. (entering with Donna Elvira, Masetto and Peasants).
Z.
An-diam, an-diam, Si - gno - ra! ve - dre - te in qual ma -
This way, Don-na El - vi - ra! I left him tied up se -
Donna Elvira.
Z. E.
nie-ra ho con-cio il scel-le - ra - to. Ah, so-pra lu - i si sfoghi il mio fu -
cure-ly. He won't es - cape us this time. Clev-er Zer - li - na! The laugh is now on
Zerlina.
Donna Elvira.
E. Z.
ror! Stel-le! in qual mo-do si sal-vò quel bric - co - ne? L'avrà sot-trat-to
him. Van-ished! But how could he? With the stool and the win-dow! His wick-ed mas-ter
Zerlina.
E. Z.
l'em-pio suo pa-dro - ne. Fu des-so sen-za fal - lo: an-che di
must have come and found him. You're right; He must have done it. They can't be
(Masetto and Peasants hasten out)
Z.
que-sto in-for-miam Don Ot - ta-vio: a lui si a-spet-ta Far per noi
far off. We must tell Don Oc - ta - vio. He swore to help us. It won't be
(Exit)
Z.
tut - ti o do - man - dar ven-det - ta!
long now. The hour of doom ap-proach-es.

No. 21c "In quali eccessi, o Numi."

Recitative and Aria.

E.
A-per-to veg-gio il ba-ra-tro mortal!
The fell a-bys-ses al-read-y yawn in wait!
tr
p
Mi-se-ra Elvi-ra! che con-tra-sto d'af-fet-ti,
Why am I trem-bling, and pos-sessed by a vi-sion?
in sen ti nasce!
I stand between them,
Per-chè que-sti so-spi-ri?
between him and re-pri-sal.
e quest' am-ba-scie?
I pray to save him!
Aria.
Mi tra-dì quell' al-ma in-
Can it be that I for-
gra-ta, quell' al-ma in-gra-ta, in-fe-li-ce, o
give him And would pro-tect him? His be-tray-al, my
Cl.
Fag.
cresc.
p cresc.

E.
Di - o! mi fa, in - fe - li - ce, o Di - o! mi fa, in - fe -
bit - ter re-proof, Are they signs from pow - ers a-bove? Thus did
Vlns.
mfp
sfp
Fag.
Cl.
mfp
li - ce, o Di-o! o Dio! mi fa.
God e-lect him To teach me love?
sfp
Fl.
Fag.
Ma tra-di-ta, e ab-ban - do-na-ta,
My pro-tec-tion, my plans to save him,
Vlns.
Fl.
Vlns.
Fl.
pro - vo an-cor per lui pie-tà, pro - vo an-cor per
Are they on - ly pit - eous pride, Pride that would it -
Cl.
Fag.
Vlns.
lui pie-tà, pro - vo an-cor per lui, per
self re-store? Are they more than Poor de -
Str.
Fag.
Cello
mfp
mf

E.
lui, per lui pie - tà. Mi tra - di quell' al - ma in - gra - ta, quell'
signs to - be his bride? No, I can - not yet for - give him, Will
Cl.
Fag.
Cl.
E.
al - ma in - gra - ta, in - fe - li - ce, o Di - o! mi fa, in - fe - li - ce, o
not pro - tect him! Though at heart I do not a - tone For the on - ly
Cl.
Fag.
cresc.
p cresc.
mfp
sfp
E.
Di - o! mi fa, in - fe - li - ce, o Di - o! o Dio! mi fa!
love I have known, Let my heart re - ject him, My love dis - own!
mfp
sfp
Cl.
Cor.
E.
Quan - do sen - to il mio tor - mento, il mio tor - mento, di ven - det - ta il
Then let rage con - sume re - gret And o - ver - take him! Rage con - sole the
Vln.
Fl.
Vln.
Cello
E.
cor fa - vel - la, ma se guar - do il suo ci - men - to,
heart's un - do - ing! Heart, when chance must At length for - sake him,
Str.

E.
pal - pi - tan - do il cor mi va, pal - pi - tan -
Shall we not our peace re - new? Shall we not
Fl.
Fag.
- do il cor, il cor mi va, il
for - get, at length for - get? I
Fag. & Cello.
cor mi va. Mi tra - dì quell'al-ma ingra-ta, quell' al - ma in-
would ... and yet Can it be that I for-give him And would pro -
Fl.
Fl.
Cl.
gra-ta, in - fe - li - ce, o Di - o! mi fa, in - fe - li - ce, o Di - o! mi
tect him? His be - tray - al, my bit - ter reproof, Are they signs from pow - ers a-
cresc.
p cresc.
mfp
sfp
fa, in - fe - li - ce, o Di - o, o Dio! mi fa!
bove? Thus did God e-lect him To teach me love?
mfp
sfp
Vlns
Cello & Wood.
sf

E.
Ma tra-di-ta, e ab-ban-do-na-ta, pro-vo an-
God of mer-cy, If I must love him, Is my
cor per lui pie-ta, per lu-i
love to guide his heart To thy love's
Fl.
Cl.
Fag.
Cello
Str.
pie-tà, pro-vo an-cor per lui pie-tà,
a-bode? Then to climb the try-ing road
pro-vo an-cor per lui pie-tà, per lui pie-tà, per
Lend my love thy strength and art, O, lend my love thy
cresc.
lui pie-tà!
strength and art!
(Exit.)

Scene.— An enclosed churchyard, several equestrian statues; statue of the Commandant; with inscription in golden lettering.
Recit.
Don Giovanni. (leaps over the wall, laughing; is still wearing Leporello's hat and cloak.)
Ah, ah, ah, ah, questa è buona, or la-scia-la cer-car; che bel-la not-te! è più chia-ra del gior-no, sembra fat-ta per gir a zon-zo a cac-cia di ra-gaz-ze.
Ha-ha, ha-ha, that was lucky! I've thrown them off the scent. How bright the moon is! It could al-most be day-light. Just the night to be on the prowl and go stalk-ing af-ter Beau-ty!
(looking at his watch.)
È tar-di? Oh, ancor non so-no due del-la not-te; a-vrei voglia un po' di sa-per come è fi-ni-to l'af-far tra Le-porello e Donn'El-vi-ra: s'egli ha a-vu-to giu-di-zio!
There's time yet. It's on-ly half-past one in the morning. I'm dy-ing to know how that tale fi-nal-ly end-ed, how Le-po-rel-lo han-dled Donn'El-vi-ra. Let us hope he enjoyed it!
Leporello. (behind the wall.)
Al-fin vuo-le ch'io fac-cia un pre-ci-pi-zio.
(He likes to see me swing-ing on the gal-lows.)
Don Giovanni.
È des-so; oh Le-po-rel-lo!
The ras-cal! Le-po-rel-lo!
Leporello. (from the wall)
Chi mi chia-ma?
Who are you, please?
Don Giovanni.
Non co-no-sci il pa-dron?
You know well who I am.
Leporello.
Co-sì nol co-nosces-si!
I don't and I don't want to!
Don Giov.
Co-me, bir-bo?
No more fool-ing!
Leporello.
Ah, sie-te voi? scu-sa-te!
Oh, so it's you. I'm sor-ry.
Don Giovanni.
Co-sa è sta-to?
Well, what hap-pened?
Leporello.
Per ca-gion
On your be-
G.
L.

L.
G.

Don Giovanni.

vos-tra io fui qua-si ac-cop-pa-to. Eb-ben, non e-ra que-sto un o-no-re per
half I came near be-ing butch-ered. But think what a great hon-or such a fate would have

G.
L.

Leporello. Don Giovanni.

te? Si-gnor, vel do-no. Via via, vien quà, vien quà! che bel-le co-se ti deg-gio
been! The thought con-soles me. Now, now, come on, come on! You look so fun-ny with a sol-emn

G.
L.

Leporello. Don Giovanni.

(Leporello climbs over the wall, and exchanges hat and cloak with Don Giovanni.)

dir. Ma co-sa fa-te qui? Vien den-tro e lo sa-pra-i: di-ver-se i-sto-riel-le
face. What *are* you do-ing *here?* Come in and I will tell you. A lot of the ad-ven-tures

G.

che accadu-te mi son dac-chè par-ti-sti, ti di-rò un' al-tra vol-ta: or la più
that have hap-pened to me since last I saw you, I must leave for the mo-ment. But there is

G.
L.

Leporello. Don Giovanni.

bel-la ti vo' so-lo nar-rar. Don-ne-sca al cer-to? C'è dub-bio? u-na fan-ciul-la,
one that will a-muse you, I know. A new young la-dy? Ex-act-ly! Such a nice mor-sel!

G.

bel-la gio-vin ga-lan-te, per la stra-da in-con-tra-hi; le va-do appresso, la
She was walk-ing a-long all by her-self when I saw her. I turned and fol-lowed. I

G.

pren-do per la man, fug-gir mi vuo-le; di-co po-che pa-ro-le, el-la mi
tried to take her hand. She start-ed run-ning. When I spoke, though, she halt-ed, mis-tak-ing

Leporello. Don Giovanni. Leporello. Don Giov. Leporel.
G. L.
pi-glia_sai per chi? Non lo sò. Per Le-po-rel-lo. Per me? Per te. Va
me for Can you guess? No, I can't! For Le-po-rel-lo! For me? For you. How
Don Giovanni. Leporello. Don Giov.
L. G.
be-ne. Per la ma-no es-sa al-lo-ra me pren-de_ An-co-ra me-glio. M'ac-ca-
fun-ny! With a cry of de-light she took my hand. I'll die of laugh-ing. She em-
G.
rez-za, mi ab-braccia: "Ca-ro il mio Le-po-rel-lo! Le-po-rel-lo, mio ca-ro!„
braced me. She kissed me. "O dear-est Le-po-rel-lo, Le-po-rel-lo, my lov-er!"
Leporello. Don Giov.
G. L.
al-lor m'accor-si ch'e-ra qual-che tua bel-la. Oh, ma-le-det-to! Dell' in-
Of course, I knew then she was one of your dain-ties. No, this is too much. Things were
G.
gan-no approfit-to; non sò co-me mi ri-co-no-sce, gri-da; sento gen-te,
go-ing so nice-ly but then, somehow, she re-cog-nized me and screamed. People heard her.
G.
a fug-gi-re mi met-to, e pron-to, pron-to perquel mu-ret-to in que-sto lo-co io
It was time to be mov-ing so, quick as light-ning, I jumped a wall and land-ed in this
Leporello. Don Giovanni. Leporello.
G. L.
mon-to. E mi di-te la co-sa con ta-le indif-fe-ren-za? Per-chè no? Ma se
graveyard. And you tell me this sto-ry as if it were a-mus-ing? And why not? But she

(The moon breaks through the clouds, and floods the statue of the Commandant with ghostly light.)
Don Giovanni (laughs loudly)
L.
G.
fos - se co - stei sta - ta mia mo - glie? Me - glio an - co - ra!
might be the girl I mean to mar - ry. So she might be!
Adagio.
The Statue.
C.
Di ri - der fi - ni - rai pria dell au - ro - - ra!
Your laugh - ter will not last, e - ven till morn - - ing.
Ob. Cl. Fag. 3 Trombones & Bassi
Don Giovanni.
Leporello.
G.
L.
Chi ha par - la - to? Ah, qual - che a - ni - ma sa - rà dell' al - tro mon - do,
Who could that be? Ah, some spir - it from the world of the de - part - ed,
Don Giovanni. (puts his hand to his sword, looks about among the tombs and strikes at some of the statues.)
L.
G.
che vi co - no - sce a fon - do. Ta - ci, sciocco! chi va là? chi va là?
where they know all a - bout you. Stop it, id - iot! Who goes there? Who goes there?
Adagio.
The Statue.
C.
Ri - bal - do au - da - ce! La - scia a' mor - ti la pa -
Re - mem - ber, re - mem - ber, that the dead still re - mem -
Leporello.
Don Giovanni.
C.
L.
G.
ce! Ve l'ho det - to! Sa - rà qual - cun di fuo - ri che si bur - la di no - i!
ber. Who's the id - iot? It's on - ly some - one out side who is try - ing to fool us.
(With indifference and disdain)
G.
Ehi, del Commenda - to - re non è que - sta la sta - tua? leg - gi un po - co quel - la iscri -
Well, the Commen da - to - re makes a beau ti - ful sta - tue. Can you read the words on the

Leporello.
G.
L.
zion. Scu-sa-te, non ho im-pa-ra-to a leg-ge-re a' rag-gi del-la
base? Ex-cuse me! I have-n't got the spec-ta-cles I wear for moonlight
Don Giovanni. (touching his sword.) Leporello. (reads the shining inscription.)
L.
G.
lu-na. Leg-gi, di-co! "Dell' em-pio, che mi tras-se al pas-so e-
read-ing. Go on! Read them! Struck down by an as-sas-sin I lie, be-
(recoils terrorstricken.)
L.
stre-mo, qui at-ten-do la ven-det-ta." U-di-ste? io tre-mo!
liev-ing that Heav-en will a-venge me. You hear that? I'm fright-ened!
Don Giovanni.
G.
O vec-chio buf-fo-nis-si-mo! di-gli che que-sta se-ra l'at-tendo a ce-nar
An ad-mir-a-ble sen-ti-ment. Ask the Com-men-da-to-re if he can come to
Leporello. (the inscription grows dim.)
G.
L.
me-co! Che paz-zia! ma mi par, Oh Dei, mi-ra-te, che ter-
sup-per. I will not. Are you mad? O God, he's watch-ing. Look how
L.
ri-bi-le oc-chia-to e-gli ci da! par vi-vo! par che sen-ta, e
stern-ly and an-gri-ly he glares. He fol-lows what we're say-ing. Sup-
Don Giovanni. (with hand on sword.)
L.
G.
che vo-glia par-lar! Or-sù, va là, o qui t'ammaz-zo, e poi ti sep-pel-
pose he were to speak! How would you like to lose your head or be chopped in lit-tle
Leporello.
G.
L.
li-sco! Pia-no, pia-no, Si-gno-re, o-ra ub-bi-di-sco.
piec-es? While I live, I will do as Mas-ter pleas-es.

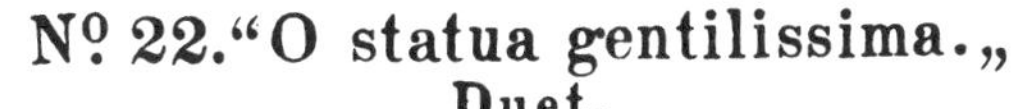

Duet.

Allegro. Leporello. (to the Commandant.)

Tutti. *f* *p* *f* *p*

O sta - tua gen - ti - lis - sima del gran Commenda - to - re _ (to Don G.) Padron! mi trema il co - re, non pos - so, non posso terminar!

O most il - lus trious mon - u - ment to our Commen da - to - re _ I can't, It makes me shud der. I can't and I won't, I won't go on.

Don Giov. Fi - ni - scila, o nel pet - to ti met - to questo acciar, ti met - to questo ac - ciar!

Wind. Cor. O yes, you will. Would you rath - er I prod ded you with this, I prod ded you with this?

cresc.

Leporello. (aside.) Che impiccio, che ca - priccio! Don Giovanni. (aside.) Che gusto! che spas - set - to! Leporello. Io sento mi ge - lar, io sen - to mi ge - lar!

He's mad and get - ting mad der. He quivers like a jel - ly. I'm froz - en stiff with fright. I'm froz - en stiff with fright.

fp

Don Giovanni. Lo voglio far tremar, lo voglio far tremar!

I shan't for get this night. I shan't for get this night.

(to the statue) O sta - tua gen - ti -

O sta - tue most il -

f *p* tr tr

(starting back)
L.
lis - sima — benchè di mar - mo siate — Ah Padron! Padron mi - o! mira - te! mi -
lus - tri - ous — of ven - er - à - ble mar - ble O dear God! Heav en save us! O master, look,
tr
tr
f
p
L.
G.
ra - te! che se - guita a guar - dar, che seguita a guar - dar!
mas - ter! The eyes be - gin to glow with an un - earth - ly light.
Don Giovanni. (advancing menacingly)
Mo - ri,
Shall I
cresc.
f
G.
L.
mori!
prod you?
Leporello.
No, no, no, no, atten - dete, at - ten - de - te!
No, please please wait a mo - ment. I'll con - tin - ue.
Str.
p
(going back)
L.
Si - gnor, il padron mi - o —
My Lord my mas - ter bids you
Wind.
Str.
p
L.
ba - da - te ben, non i - o —
(My mas - ter bids, not I, sir,) —
Wind.

(The statue nods its head)
vor - ria con voi ce - nar! Ah! ah! ah! _ che scena è
to sup with him to - night. Ah! Ah! Ah! _ I swear he
questa! ah, ah, ah, _ che sce-na è que-sta! o ciel! chi - nò la
nodded. Ah! Ah Ah! _ I swear he nod-ded As if . . . he had ac-
Don Giovanni. (not looking at him)
Va là, che sei un buf - fo - ne, va là, che sei un buf - fo - ne, un buf -
Oh, pull your-self to - geth-er. Stop be - ing so ri - dic - u - lous, You're
te - sta!
cept - ed.
cresc.
Leporello.
fo - ne, un buf - fo - ne! Guar-da-te, guar-da-te, guar-da-te an-cor, pa -
talk-ing sil - ly non-sense. But watch it. Look, mas-ter, and you will see what
f
p
Don Giovanni.
dro - ne! E che deg-gio guar-dar, deggio guardar, deg-gio guar-dar?
I saw. To see cold mar-ble move is not a sight that I would miss.
cresc.
f

Leporello.
(imitates the statue)
(the statue bends its head)
L.
Col-la mar-mo-rea testa ei fa co - sì, co - sì.
Mar-ble or not, it nod-ded. It moved like this, like this.
p
mf
p
p
D. Giov.
(sees the statue)
G.
Col - la mar-mo - - rea testa ei fa co - sì, co - sì.
Mar - ble or not, it nod-ded. It moved like this, like this.
L.
Col - la mar-mo - - rea testa ei fa co - sì, co - sì.
Mar - ble or not, it nod-ded. It moved like this, like this.
f
p
Don Giovanni. (to the statue)
G.
Par -
Speak
la - te! se po - te - te.
up, sir! I can't hear you.
cresc.
f
Ver - re - te a ce - na? ver - re - te a ce - na?
Have you ac - cept ed my in - vi - ta - tion?

mezza voce
The Statue. (inclining its head.)
Don Giovanni.
C. G.
Sì! Bi - zar-ra è in ver la
Yes! Was ev - er such a
Leporello.
L.
Mo - - - - ver mi pos - so ap - pe - na, mi
Oh how my heart is beat - ing. Pre -
sf
fp
Cor.
G.
sce - na, ver - rà il buon vecchio, il buon vec - chio a
meet - ing. Who saw a sta - tue of mar - ble
man - ca, o Dei, la le - na! mi man - ca, o Dei, la
vent, O God, this meet - ing! Pre - vent, O God, this
ce - na. A pre - pa - rar - la an - dia - mo, a pre - pararla an -
eat - ing? Come, we must go this mo - ment And hur - ry to make
lena! Per cari - tà, par - tiamo, per ca - ri - tà, par - tiamo, an - diamo via di
meeting! What shall I do? Then tell me. I hope that you can tell me. What am I to make
dia - mo, par - tia - mo via di quà! Bi - zar - ra è in ver la
read - y to greet our wor - thy guest. Was ev - er such a
quà! an - diamo, andia - mo via di quà! per ca - ri - tà, par - tiamo, andiamo via di
read - y, what am I to serve your guest? I hope that you can tell me What I should serve your

G.
sce - na, ver - rà il buon vec-chio a ce - na; A
meet - ing. Who saw a sta - tue eat - ing? Pre -
L.
quà, per ca - ri - tà, par - tiamo, andiamo via di quà, andiamo via di
guest? I hope that you can tell me What should I serve your guest? What should I serve your
G.
pre - parar - la an-diamo, partia - mo via di quà, par -
pare, pre-pare, get read - y to greet our wor-thy guest, To
L.
quà! andiamo via di quà, andiamo, andiamo via di quà, an-diamo, andiamo via di
guest? I hope that you can tell me, you can tell me, you can tell me, you can tell me, you can
G.
tia - mo via di quà.
greet our wor - thy guest.
(Exeunt.)
L.
quà, via di quà, via di quà, di quà, di quà, di quà!
tell, you can tell, you can tell, What shall I serve your guest?
pp
Recit.
(A room. The moon is shining through the casement.)
Don Octavio.
O.
Calma-tevi, i-dol mi - o! di quel ri - baldo vedrem puni - ti in bre - ve i gra - vi eccessi,
Be com-fort-ed, my dear-est, for ver - y soon the long arm of Jus-tice will reach out to take him
Donna Anna.
Don Octavio.
O.
A.
ven-di - ca - ti sarem. Ma il padre, o Di - o! Con - vien chi - na - re il ci - glio al vo -
and your wrong be a-venged. But fath-er! Poor fath-er! What - ev - er be our por-tion, we must

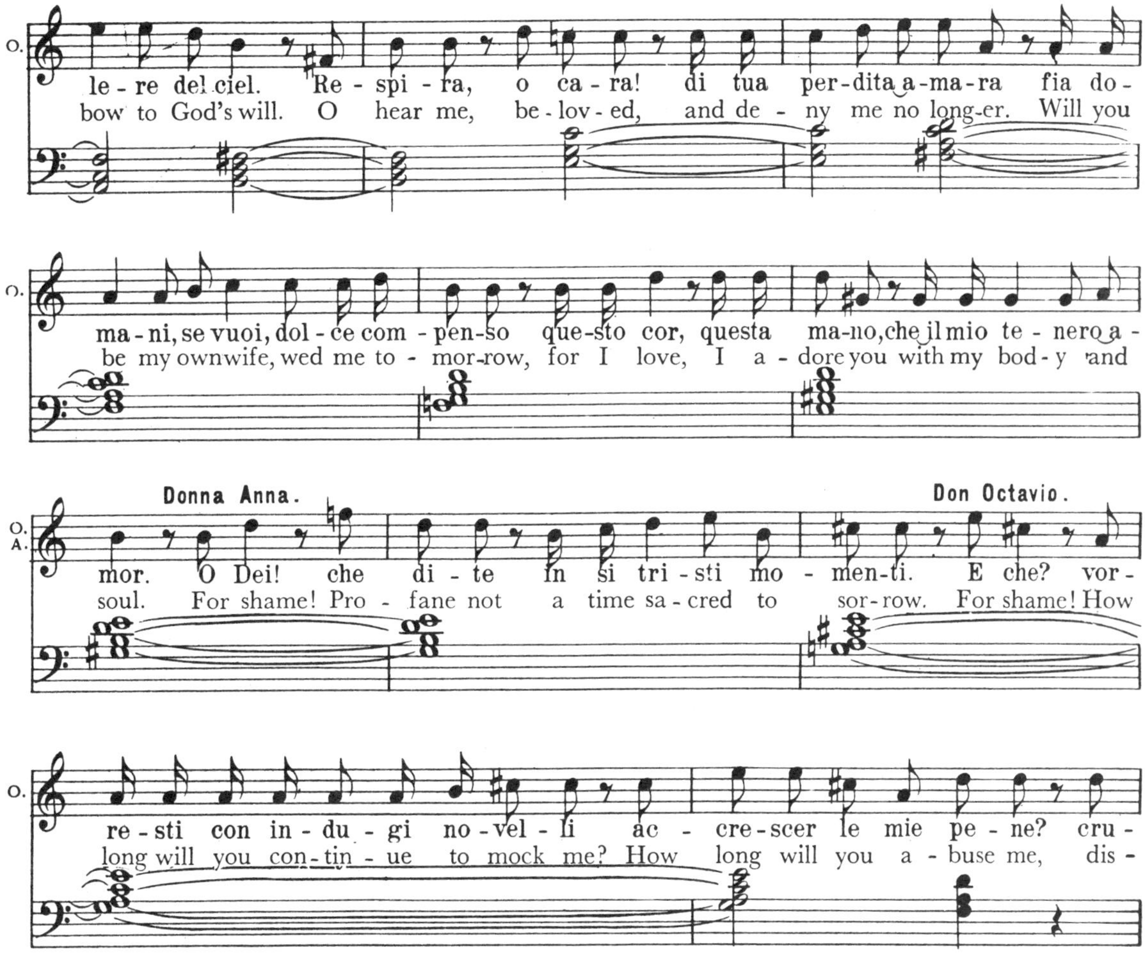

O.

le - re del ciel. Re - spi - ra, o ca - ra! di tua per - dita a - ma - ra fia do -
bow to God's will. O hear me, be - lov - ed, and de - ny me no long - er. Will you

O.

ma - ni, se vuoi, dol - ce com - pen - so que - sto cor, questa ma - no, che il mio te - nero a -
be my own wife, wed me to - mor - row, for I love, I a - dore you with my bod - y and

Donna Anna. Don Octavio.

O. A.

mor. O Dei! che di - te in si tri - sti mo - men - ti. E che? vor -
soul. For shame! Pro - fane not a time sa - cred to sor - row. For shame! How

O.

re - sti con in - du - gi no - vel - li ac - cre - scer le mie pe - ne? cru -
long will you con - tin - ue to mock me? How long will you a - buse me, dis -

Nº 23. "Crudele?"

Recitative and Aria.

A.
Ma il mondo, oh Di - o! non se -
But hear me! Re mem - ber, when the
f
p
dur la co-stan-za del sen-si - bil mio core; ab-ba-stan - za per te mi parla a -
jeal-ous mis-giv - ings of a lov - er be-set you, all the stars shall fall down ere I for -
sf
p
mo-re!
get you.
Larghetto.
Cl.
Fag.
Vln.
sotto voce
Fl.
Non mi
Let yon-der
dir, bell' i - dol mi - o, che son i - o cru-del con
moon, chaste eye of Heav - en, Cool de - sire and calm your
mf
mfp
te, tu ben sa - i quant' io t'a -
soul; May the bright stars their pa-tience
Str.
Fag.
Cor.

A.
ma - i, tu co-no-sci la mia fè, tu co -
lend you, As their con stel la - tions roll, Turn, turn,
Fag.
Cl.
Fl.
no - sci la mia fè.
turn- a - bout the Pole.
Cal - ma,
Far, too
Cl.
Fag.
Fl. Fag.
calma il tuo tor - mento,
far they seem from our dy ing,
Se di duol non vuoi ch'io
Cold, we call them, to our
mo - ra, se di duol non vuoi ch'io mo - ra, non vuoi ch'io mo - ra.
sigh - ing; We, too proud, too e - vil-mind ed, By sin are blind-ed.
Fag.
Violin
cresc.
f
Non mi dir, bell' i - dol mi - o, che son
See how bright the moon shines yon - der, Si - lent
p

A.
i - o cru - del con te; cal - ma, cal - ma il tuo tor -
wit-ness to all our wrong: Ah! but heark-en! O bless-ed
mf
sf
p
Cor. sustain
men - to, se di duol non vuoi ch'io
won-der! Out of si - - - lence comes a
mo - ra, non vuoi ch'io mo - - ra!
mu - sic, And I can hear her song.
f
p
mfp
Allegretto moderato.
Vns.
p
Wind.
For - se, forse un giorno il cie - lo an -
God will surely, surely wipe a - way thy tears, my -

A.

co - ra sen - ti - rà, sen-ti - rà pie - tà di me! forse un
daugh - ter; On thy dark, On thy dark, His light shall break. God is

giorno il cielo an-co-ra sen-ti - rà
Watching thee, hath not for - gotten thee. On thy dark

p

pie - tà di me, sen - ti - rà pie -
His light shall break. On my dark, On my

tà, pie - tà di me, sen - ti -
dark, His light shall break, On my

cresc. *sfp* *p*

A.
rà — pie - tà di me, — for-se, for-se il cie - lo un
dark, His — light shall break, God will heed me, sus - tain me, con -
Vln.
Wind
sf
p
gior-no sen - ti - rà — pie - tà — di
sole me. On my dark, — His — light — shall
fp
tr
me, sen - ti - rà pie - tà di me, pie - tà — di —
break, On my dark, His light shall break, His — light — shall —
fp
p
cresc.
me.
break. (Exit.)
f
Recit.
Don Octavio. (alone)
O.
Ah, si se-gua il suo pas - so: Io vo' con le - i di - vi - de - rei mar -
Ah! The heav - ens have spok - en! That sa - cred har - mo - ny seemed to me a
ti - ri: Sa - ran me - co men gra - vi i suoi so - spi - ri.
tok - en, A sweet prom - ise of mar - riage, not to be brok - en. (Exit.)

Nº 24. "Già la mensa e preparata.,,
Finale.

A lighted hall. The table prepared for a banquet.

(to Leporello)
Leporello.
G.
L.
Leporel-lo, presto in ta-vola! Son prontis - simo a ser - vir, son pron-
Le-po-rel-lo! serve im-mediate-ly. Com-ing, sir, with out de - lay. Com - ing,
Don Giovanni. (to Lep.)
tis - simo a ser-vir. Giac - chè spen-do i miei da - na - ri, io mi
sir, with-out de-lay. We have all the night be - fore us: Let us
f
p
cresc.
(to the musicians)
vo - glio di - ver - tir. Voi suo-na - te, a-mi - ci ca - ri! Giacchè
hear how you can play. Come, my friends, strike up a meas-ure! We have
spen-do i miei da - na-ri, io mi vo-glio di - ver-tir, io mi voglio di - ver-
all the night be - fore us: Let us hear how you can play. Let us hear how you can
Allegretto.
Leporello.
tir. (The private band begins the first piece,
play. melody from Martin's Una cosa rara.)
Bravi! "Cosa rara!„
Mar-tin Co-sa ra-ra
Ob.
(Music on stage: 2 Ob., Clar., Bassoons, Horns.)

Don Giov.
G.
Che ti
Don't you
f
(eating; to Lep.)
G.
L.
par del bel con-cer - to?
think these fel-lows play well?
Leporello.
È con-for - me, è con-for-me al vo - stro
So they should, So they should; they know you
Don Giovanni.
L.
G.
merto. Ah che piatto sa-po - ri-to! ah che piatto sa-po - ri-to! ah che piatto sa-po-
pay well. Ah, how perfect ly de - li-cious! Ah, how per-fect-ly de - li-cious! Ah, how perfect-ly de-
p
ri - to!
li - cious!
Leporello. (aside)
Ah che bar-baro appe - ti - to!
All his ap-pe-tites are vi - cious.
p
L.
Che boc - co - ni da gi - gan - te! mi par proprio di sve - nir, mi par proprio di sve-
I can hard - ly bear to watch - him, Watch him guzzling in that way, Watch him guzzling in that

Don Giovanni. (aside)
nir. Nel ve-der i miei boc-co - ni, gli par proprio di sve-nir, gli par proprio di sve-
way. How he watch-es ev - ry mouth-ful. He would like some, I dare-say. He would like some, I dare -
pp
sf
p
sf
p
Leporello
Don Giov.
nir. Ah che bar-baro appe - ti - to! che boc-co-ni da gi-gante! Nel ve-
say. All his ap-pe-tites are vi-cious. I can hard-ly bear to watch him, How he
cresc.
f
p
sf
Leporello.
der i miei boc-co - ni, gli par proprio di svenir, di sve-nir! Ah che bar-baro appe-
watch-es ev - ry mouth ful. He would like some, I dare-say. I dare-say. All his ap-pe-tites are
Don Giovanni.
Leporello.
Don Giovanni.
ti - to! Gli par proprio di sve-nir. Che boc-co-ni da gi-gan-te! Gli par proprio di sve-
vi-cious. He would like some, I dare say. I can hard-ly bear to watch him He would like some, I dare-
nir, gli par proprio di sve-nir, gli par proprio di sve-nir.
say. He would like some, I dare-say. He would like some, I dare-say.
Leporello. mi par proprio di sve-nir, mi par proprio di sve-nir.
Watch him guz-zling in that way, Watch him guz-zling in that way.
(The private band finishes the first piece.)
p Strings in Orch.

(The private band begins the 2d. piece. from Paisiello's
Fra i due litiganti il terzo gode.)
Don Giovanni.
Leporello.
Piat-to!
Serve me!
Servo!
Here, sir.
Allegretto.
Leporello.
Ev - vi-va-noi li-ti-ganti.
From Sar-ti's I Li-ti-gan-ti.
Don Giovanni.
Ver - sa il vi-no!
Pour the clar-et.
Ec - cel - len-te
Wine and wom-en
mar-zi - mino!
both are pleas-ant.
(Leporello changes Giovanni's plate)
Leporello (aside)
Que - sto pez-zo
Why should he have
di fa-giano, pia - no, piano, piano, piano, pia-no vo'inghiot-tir.
all this pheas-ant? Just one ti-ny, ti-ny, ti-ny, ti - ny bit for me!
Don Giovanni.
Sta man-
Steal - ing

(aside)
G.
giando quel mar - rano! fin - ge - rò di non ca - pir.
tid-bits like a peas-ant. Think-ing that I can - not see.
(Private band finishes the second piece.)
f
p Strings in Orch.
L.
Leporello.
Moderato.
(Private band begins the 3d. piece, from Mozart's Figaro.)
Questo
Fi - ga -
Cl.
f
p
poi la co - no - sco pur troppo.
ro, that is so o - ver-rat - ed!
mf
p
Don Giovanni (without looking at him)
Leporello. (with his mouth full)
Le - po - rel - lo! Pa - dron mi - o!
Le - po - rel - lo! At your serv - ice.
tr
f
p
Don Giovanni.
Leporello. (clearing his throat.)
Par - la schietto, par - la schietto, mascal - zo - ne. Non mi la - scia una flus -
Speak more clear-ly, Speak more clear-ly, I can't hear you. I have caught a cold, I
p
Cl.
tr

Don Giov.
L.
G.
sione le pa-ro-le pro-fe-rir, le pa-ro-le pro-ferir. Mentre io
think, sir. For I'm hoarse, as hoarse can be, For I'm hoarse, as hoarse can be. While I'm
tr
cresc.
f
p
Leporello.
Don Giov. (looking towards him)
mangio fischia un po-co. Non sò far. Cos' è?
eating, whis-tle some-thing! But I can't. You can't?
cresc.
Leporello.
Scusa-te! scu-sa-te! sì ec-cel-len-te è'l vo-stro cuo-co, sì ec-cel-
He's caught me! Now look, sir. You have of-ten praised your cook, sir, You have
f
p
lente, sì eccellen-te è'l vo-stro cuo-co, che lo volli anch'io pro-var, che lo volli anch'io pro-
of-ten, ver-y of-ten praised your cook, sir, So I wanted to sample this cooking. And I took the lib-er-
mf
p
Don Giovanni.
Sì eccel-lente è il cuo-co mi-o, che lo volle anch' ei pro-
You believed that I was-n't looking So you took the lib-er-
var, sì eccellen-te, che lo volli anch'io pro-
ty. Were you looking? Yes, I took the lib-er-
mf
p

Allegro assai.
Donna Elvira. (rushes in distractedly)
E.
G.
L.
L'ul-ti-ma pro-va dell' a-mor mi-o an-cor vogl'
Dreams of dis-as-ter, Vi-sions of hor-ror, Drive me to
var.
ty.
(Exeunt all servants but Leporello.)
var.
ty.
(The private band finishes the 3d piece.)
Allegro assai.
Tutti
f
p
i-o fa-re con te. Più non ram-men-to gl'in-gan-ni
seek you, Lov-er un-true: Not to re-proach you, Not for my
tr
tuo-i, gl'in-gan-ni tuo-i, pie-ta-de io
own sake Am I come hith-er, I've come to
cresc.
(kneeling)
sen-to! Da te non
warn you . . . Hear, I im-
Don Giovanni. (rising and dismissing the players with a sign.)
Cos' è? Cos' è?
To warn? Of what?
Leporello.
Cos' è? Cos' è?
To warn? Of what?
cresc.

(distant thunder of an approaching storm.)
E.
chie - de quest' alma oppres - sa del - la sua fe - de qual - che mer -
plore you, One who a - dored you, For your im - mor - tal Soul I
sf
sf
p
Don Giovanni. (trying to raise her.)
E.
G.
cè. Mi ma - ra - vi - glio! co - sa vo - le - te? co - sa vo -
sue. Why this re - cum - bent, Pi - ous po - si - tion? Is it be -
f
p
p
p
f
p
G.
(kneels)
le - te? Se non sor - ge - te non re - sto in piè, non re - sto in
com - ing? If you pre - fer it, I will kneel too. I will kneel
cresc.
f
Donna Elvira.
G.
E.
piè! Ah non de - ri - de - re gli af - fan - ni mie - i!
too. Ah, do not mock at my Dread pre - mo - ni - tion!
Leporello.
L.
Qua - si da
My eyes are
p
p
E.
Don Giovanni. (He gets up and raises her)
Ah, non de - ri - de - re!
Ah, do not mock at me!
G.
Io ti de - ri - de - re!
Why should I mock at you?
L.
pian - ge - re mi fa co - ste - i, qua -
wa - ter - ing For this poor la - dy! My
tr
tr

E.
G.
L.
(With affected tenderness)
Ah non de - ri - de-re!
Ah, do not mock at me!
Io te de - ri - de-re?
Why should I mock at you?
Cie-lo! per - chè?
Dear, it's not true.
si da pian - ge - re mi fa co - ste-i.
eyes are wa - ter - ing For this poor la-dy!
tr
cresc.
Don Giovanni.
Che vuoi, mio be - ne?
My love, what is it?
Che vi - ta can - gi!
Be - ware God's an - ger!
p
Cor per - fi - do!
Be - ware of it!
Bra - va!
Bra - vo!
fp
Cor per - fi - do! cor per - - -
Be - ware of it! Be - ware
Leporello.
Bra - va!
Bra - vo!
Cor per - - -
Be - ware
f

E.
- fi-do!
of it!
Don Giovanni. (turning toward the table).
L.
G.
- fi-do! La - - scia ch'io man-gi,
of it! Af - - ter the bran-dy,
tr
p
G.
la - - scia ch'io man-gi,
Not while I'm eat-ing:
(seats himself again at the table, and begins to eat)
Vns.
mf
p
Donna Elvira. (with disdain).
E.
Res-ta-ti, bar-ba-ro!
Lost, then e - ter-nal-ly,
Leporello.
G.
L.
e se ti pia - ce, man-gia con me!
If you feel hun-gry, Then come and eat too.
Se - non si -
Cold must that
f
p
E.
nel lez-zo im - mon-do e - sem - pio or - ri-bi-le d'i-ni-qui-
Wal - low in lewd-ness, Flaunt your in - iq-ui-ty, Roll in your
L.
muo - ve del suo do - lo - re, di sasso ha il co - re, o cor non
man be, Heart-less as marble, Who with-out pit - y Mocks her
cresc.

E.
tà!
sty!
Don Giovanni. (recklessly raising his glass).
L.
G.
ha! Vi - van le fem-mi - ne, vi - va il buon vi - no!
cry. Hon-our and glo - ry to Song, Wine and Wom-en!
p
f
so-stegno e glo - ri - a d'u - ma - ni - tà, so-stegno e glo - ri - a
May I en - joy them all Un - til I die. May I en - joy them all
cresc.
f
p
Donna Elvira.
Re - sta - ti, bar - ba - ro! nel
Lost, then e - ter - nal - ly, Wal -
d'u-ma - ni - tà! Vi - van le fem-mi - ne,
Un-til I die. Long may I hon-our them,
Leporello.
Se non si muo - ve
How cold he must be,
fp
fp
p
fp
lez - zo im - mon - do, re - sta - ti, bar - ba - ro!
low in lewd - ness, Lost, then e - ter - nal - ly,
vi - va il buon vi - no! vi - van le
Song, Wine and Wom - en. Long may I
del suo do - lo - re, di sas - so
Heart - less as mar - ble, to mock her,
fp
p
fp
fp

E.
nel lez-zo im mon-do! e - - sem-pio or - ri - bi-le
Wal - low in lewd-ness, Flaunt your in - iq - ui-ty,
G.
fe - mi - ne vi-va il buon vi - no! so - ste-gno e glo - ri-a
hon - our them, Song, Wine and Wom-en! May I en - joy them all
L.
ha il co - re, di sas-so ha il co - re, o
to mock her, So heart - less - ly to
fp
fp
p
tr
cresc.
d'i - ni - qui - tà!
Roll in your sty!
d'u - ma - ni - tà,
Un - til I die.
so - ste-gno e glo - ri - a d'u - ma - ni-
May I en-joy them all Un - til I
cor non ha.
mock her cry.
f
p
e - sem-pio or - ri - bi - le d'i - ni - qui - tà, d'i - ni - qui-
Flaunt your in - iq - ui - ty, Roll in your sty! Roll in your
tà, so - steg-no e glo - ri - a d'u - ma - ni - tà, d'u - ma - ni-
die. May I en - joy them all Un - til I die, Un - til I
Di sasso ha il co - re, o cor non ha! o cor non
With heart of mar - ble, He mocks her cry, He mocks her
mf
p
f
p

(going out of mid-
tà, dì - ni - qui - tà, e - sem - pio o - ri - bi - le d'i - ni - qui - tà!
sty! Roll in your sty! Flaunt your in - iq - ui - ty, Roll in your sty!
tà, d'u - ma - ni - tà, so - ste - gno e glo - ri - a d'u - ma - ni - tà!
die, Un - til I die. May I en - joy them all Un - til I die.
ha, o cor non ha, di sasso ha il co - re, o cor non ha!
cry, Her anguished cry. With heart of - mar - ble, Mocks her cry.
cresc.
dle door, recoils terrified)
D. Elvira. (rushes out at the opposite side)
Don Giovanni.
Ah!
Ah!
Che gri - do è que - sto
That cry was not in
Leporello.
Che
That
ma - i? che gri - do, che gri - do è que - sto ma - i? va a ve-
an - ger. What scared her, What scared her so, I won - der? Run and
(to Lep.)
gri - do è que - sto ma - i! che gri - do è que - sto ma - i?
cry was not in an - ger. What scared her so, I won - der?
der, va a ve - der che cosa è sta - to.
see, run and see what is the mat - ter.
(Leporello goes, and when off the stage cries out)

Don Giovanni.
G.
Leporello.
Che gri - do in - dia - vo - la - to! che gri - do in - dia - vo -
What can be go - ing on there? What can be go - ing
L.
Ah!
Ah!
sfp
p
cresc.
la - to! Lepo - rel - lo, che cos' è? che cos' è? che cos'
on there? Le - po - rel - lo, are you mad? Why that look? Why that
f
p
Leporello. Allegro molto
G.
L.
è? Ah! Si - gnor! per ca - ri - tà! non an-
yell? Ah . . . O God . . . Keep him a - way . . . Don't go
(Leporello returns dismayed and shuts the door.)
p
da - te fuor di quà! L'uom di sas - so, l'uo - mo
near that door I say . . . Slow - ly, sure - ly, he draws
bian - co, ah! pa - dro - ne! io ge - lo, io man - co. Se ve-
near - er He . . . the sta - tue . . . of mar - ble . . . who nod - ded. I could

Don Giov.
L.
G.
de - ste che fi - gu - ra se sen - ti - ste, co - me fa, ta, ta, ta, ta! Non ca-
see him in the moon-light I could hear each mar-ble shoe. Ta. Ta. Ta. Ta. Nev - er
cresc.
pi - sco niente af - fat - to. Tu sei mat - to in ve - ri - tà, in ve - ri -
have I heard such non sense! I shall soon go cra - zy too, go cra - zy
Leporello.
Ta, ta, ta, ta!
Ta. Ta. Ta. Ta.
f
p
cresc.
f
Leporello.
Don Giovanni.
tà, in ve - ri - tà! Ah! sen - ti - te! Qualcun bat - te!
too, go cra - zy too. There, now. Lis - ten! Someone's knock - ing.
(knocking heard at the door.)
tr
sf
p
f
Don Giov.
Leporello. (trembling)
Don Giov.
Leporello.
(kneeling)
G.
L.
Apri! Io tre - mo! A - pri, di - co! Ah!
An - swer. O mas - ter! Did you hear me? No!
p
f
p
f
Don Giov.
Leporello.
Don Giovanni.
Apri! Ah! Matto! Per to - gliermi d'in - tri - co ad a - prir io stesso an-
An - swer! No! Id - iot! Come, pull yourself to - geth - er, While I see myself who's
p
f
p

(takes a light and goes to open the door)
Leporello. (trembling, aside)
drò, io stes-so an-drò. Non vo' più veder la-mi-co, pian pia-nin m'a-scon-de-
there, who's stand-ing there. When I've pulled myself to-geth-er I shall crawl in o-ver
Strs.
cresc.
f
p
Andante. (The ghost of the Commandant appears as a marble statue.)
(Don G. opens)
The Commandant.
rò, m'a-scon-de-rò! (Leporello hides under the table)
there, crawl o-ver there.
Don Gio-
Don Gio-
(clap of thunder)
Tutti.
ff Tutti Tromboni Tympani &c.
van-ni a ce-nar te-co m'in-vi-ta-sti! e son ve-nu-to!
van-ni, I gave my prom-ise When in-vit-ed, to share your ta-ble.
Strs.
p Wind
Don Giovanni (striving to collect himself)
Non l'avrei giammai cre-du-to; ma fa-rò quel che po-trò. Leporel-lo! un altra
Who would ev-er have be-lieved it! I must do the best I can. Leporel-lo, look a-
ce-na! fa che su-bi-to si por-ti!
live, man. Set a sec-ond cov-er quick-ly!
Leporello (puts his head from under the table)
Ah padron, ah pa-dron! Ah padron! siam tutti
O I daren't. O I daren't. O I daren't. I know he'll

Don Giovanni.
(He rises as if to obey)
The Commandant.
(Don Giov. starts; Leporello retreats to back.)
L.
G.
C.
mor-ti. Van-ne, di-co! Fer-ma un po'! Non si pa-sce di ci-bo mor-
kill us. Did you hear me? Stay where you are! Those who take of the bread ev-er-
Timp.
Tutti
fp
C.
ta - - - - le, chi si pa-sce di ci-bo ce-le-ste!
last - - - - ing Need no tem-po-ral sub-stance to feed them.
Al - tre cu - re, più gra - vi di
Not for feast - ing have I now de-
cresc.
p
que - ste, al - tra bra - ma quag-
scend - - ed, Grav - - er rea - - sons have
giù mi gui-dò. Par-la
called me to earth. Well, what
Leporello.
La ter-za-na da-ve-re mi
Like a man who is sick of a

G.
dun - que! che chie - di? che
are they? Your rea - sons? Con -
C.
L.
sem-bra, e le mem-bra fer-mar più non sò, la ter-za-na d'a-ve-re mi
fe - ver, All my limbs do is trem-ble and shake. Like a man who is sick of a
vuo - i?
tin - ue.
The Commandant.
Par - lo; a - scol - ta! più tem - po non
Mark well my mes - sage for short is your
sem-bra, e le mem-bra fer-mar più non sò.
fe - ver, All my limbs do is trem-ble and shake.
Wind sustain.
(angrily and defiantly; he is quite cool again).
Par-la, par- la, a-scoltan - do ti sto.
Speak your mes-sage for short is my time.
ho.
time.
Par - lo; a -
Mark well my
Ah le membra fermar più non sò; la ter-za-na d'a-ve-re mi
All my limbs do is tremble and shake. Like a man who is sick of a
cresc.
p

C.
scol - - ta! più tem - - po non
mes - - sage for short is your
L.
sem-bra, la ter-za-na d'a-ve-re mi sem-bra, e le membra fer-mar più non
fe-ver, Like a man who is sick of a fe-ver, All my limbs do is tremble and
cresc.
p
cresc.
p
Don Giovanni.
ho. Par-la, par-la, a-scol-tan-do ti sto.
time. Speak your mes-sage for short is my time.
sò!
shake.
The Commandant.
Tu m'in-vi-ta-sti a ce-na,
He whom you have in-vit-ed
f
cresc.
il tuo do-ver or sa-i, ri-spon-di-
Brings you this in-vi-ta-tion. So an-swer
fp
f
p
mi, ri-spon-di-mi, ver-ra-i tu a ce-nar
me! So an-swer me! Will you sit down at his
f
p
cresc.
p

Don Giovanni. (calmly and coldly.)
me-co?
ta-ble?
A tor-to di vil-
No man has called me
Leporello. (standing far off, trembling)
Oi-bò, oi-bò; tempo non ha, scu-sa-te.
No, don't No, don't; tell him you have no time now.
ta-te taccia-to mia sa-rò!
cow-ard And shall not while I live.
The Commandant.
(impatiently)
Ho già ri-sol-to.
I have de-cid-ed.
Ri-sol-vi!
De-cide, then!
Ver-
You'll
The Commandant.
Don Giovanni.
ra-i?
come, then?
Ho fer-mo il co-re in pet-to, Non ho ti-
No man shall call me cow-ard. I feel no
Leporello.
Di-te di no, di-te di no!
Tell him you won't! Tell him you won't!
Vns.
(giving his right hand)
mor- ver-rò!
fear. I will.
Ec-co-la!
Cer-tain-ly...
The Commandant. (offering his left hand)
Dam-mi la ma-no in pe-gno!
Give me your hand and swear it.
Wind.

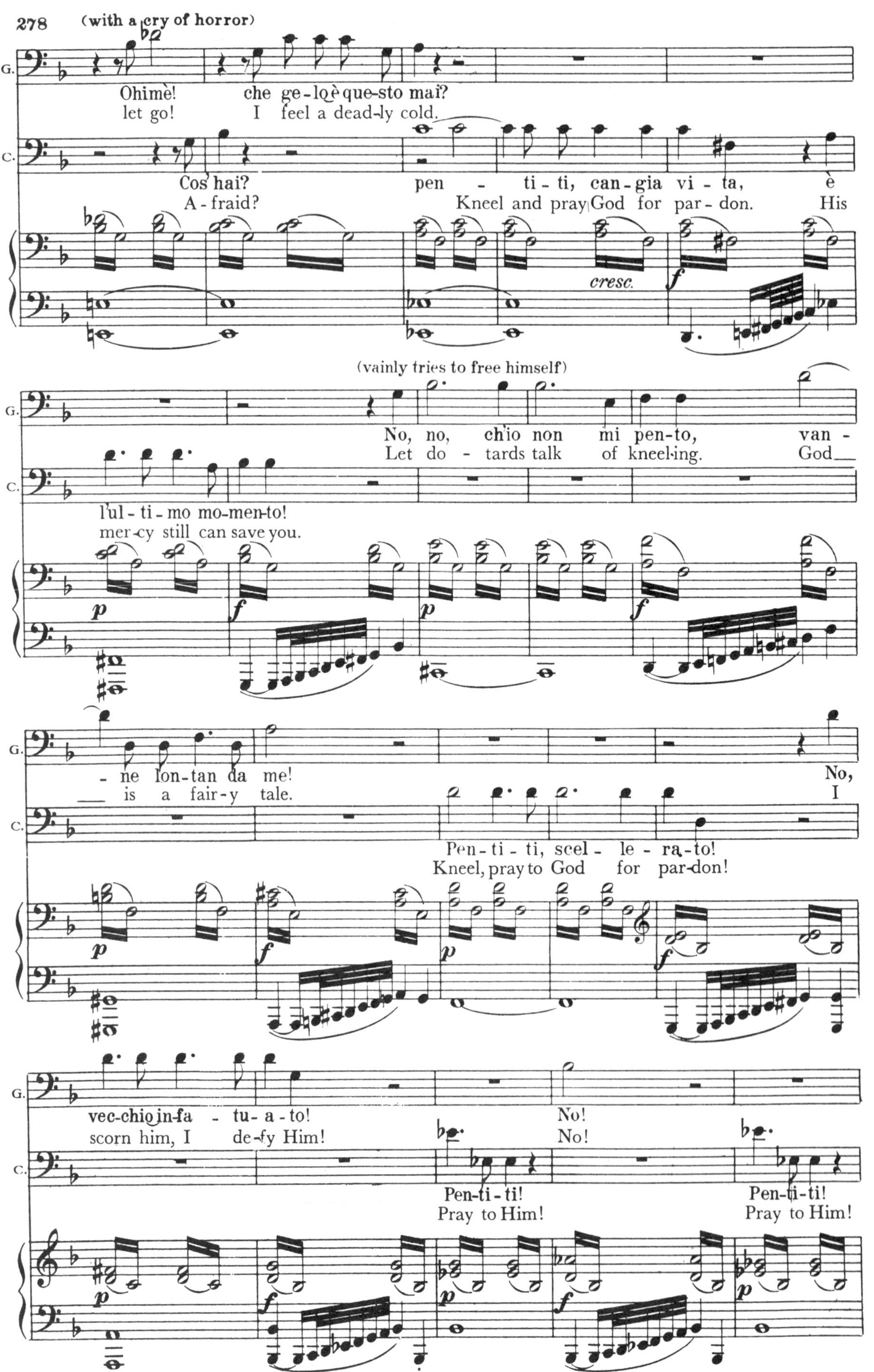
(with a cry of horror)
G.
Ohimè! che ge-lo è que-sto mai?
let go! I feel a dead-ly cold.
C.
Cos'hai? pen - ti-ti, can-gia vi-ta, è
A-fraid? Kneel and pray God for par-don. His
cresc.
(vainly tries to free himself)
No, no, ch'io non mi pen-to, van-
Let do - tards talk of kneel-ing. God
l'ul-ti-mo mo-men-to!
mer-cy still can save you.
-ne lon-tan da me!
is a fair-y tale.
Pen-ti-ti, scel - le-ra-to!
Kneel, pray to God for par-don!
No,
I
vec-chio in-fa - tu-a-to!
scorn him, I de-fy Him!
No!
No!
Pen-ti-ti!
Pray to Him!
Pen-ti-ti!
Pray to Him!

G.
C.
No!
No!
Sì!
Pray!
no!
No!
sì!
Pray!
(wresting his hand away, with a terrible cry.)
No!
No!
Sì!
Pray!
sì!
Pray!
no!
No!
no!
No!
Ah!
Your
tem -
hour
po
of
più
doom
non
is
v'è!
come.
(Exit.)
Allegro.
Don Giovanni. (in desperation.)
Da qual tremo - re in-
Fin-gers of ter - ror
(Flames appear in all directions,
the earth trembles)
so - li - to
clutch at me,
sento assa - lir gli
Hor-ri - ble fac - es
spi - ri - ti!
grin at me,
don -
A

G.
d'e-sco-no quei vor-ti-ci di fo - co pien d'or-ror?
cha-sm yawns to swal-low me, A gulf of blaz - ing fire.
Chorus (from below with hollow voices)
Tut-to a tue col-pe è po - co!
Worse pains than these a - wait thee;
p
f
p cresc.
sf
Chi Des-
vie - ni! c'è un mal peg - gior!
En - ter th'un-dy - ing fire.
l'a - nima mi la - cera? Chi m'a - gi - ta le vi - scere? Che
pair commands me ut - ter ly, My bow - els melt in ag - o ny, Un-
Leporello.
L.
Che cef - fo di - spe - ra - to! Che ge - sti da dan -
Too late, in des - per - a - tion He sees his own dam -
stra - zio, ohimè, che sma - nia! Che in - fer - no, che ter -
dy - ing pains a - wait me, In dark - ness, ice and
na - to! che gri - di! che la - men - ti!
na - tion, The house of lam - en - ta - tion,

G.
ror! Chi
fire. Des-

L.
co - me mi fa ter - ror, mi fa ter - ror!
Dark - ness and lakes of fire, red lakes of fire.

Chorus of Spirits.
Tut - to a tue col - pe è
Worse pains than these a -

sf sf sf sf

G.
l'a - nima mi la - cera? Chi m'a - gi - ta le
pair commands me ut - ter-ly, My bow - els melt in

L.
Che eef - fo - di - spe - ra - to! Che
Too late, in des - per - a - tion He

po - co! Vie - ni! c'è un mal peg - gior!
wait thee; En - ter th'un - dy - ing fire.

sf sf sf sf f

G.
vi - scere? che stra - zio, ohimè, che sma - nia! Ah!
ag - o - ny, Un - dy - ing pains a - wait me, Ah!

L.
ge - sti da dan - na - to! che gri - di! che la - men - ti! che
sees his own dam - na - tion, The house of lam - en - ta - tion, E -

G.
che in - fer - no! che ter - ror!
the dark - ness! Ah the fire!
L.
gri - di! che la - menti! co - me mi fa ter - ror!
ter - nal des - o - la - tion, Dark-ness and lakes of fire.
Vie - ni! vie - ni! vie - ni! c'è un mal peg -
En - ter! En - ter! En - ter th'un - dy - ing
D. Giov.
(The flames increase and engulf Don Giovanni)
Leporello.
G.
L.
Ah! Ah!
Ah! Ah!
gior!
fire.
sf
p
f
p
cresc.
Allegro assai.
Donna Elvira and Zerlina.
E.
Z.
Ah! dov' è il
Where is the
Don Octavio.
O.
(All enter, accompanied by ministers of justice.)
Ah! dov' è il
Where is the
Masetto.
M.
Ah! dov' è il
Where is the
Allegro assai.
f
f

E.
Z.
perfido? dov' è l'indegno? tutto il mio sdegno
wicked one? Where is he hiding? We come for vengeance,
O.
perfido? dov' è l'indegno? tutto il mio sdegno
wicked one? Where is he hiding? We come for vengeance,
M.
perfido? dov' è l'indegno? tutto il mio sdegno
wicked one? Where is he hiding? We come for vengeance,
tr
E.
Z.
A.
Donna Anna.
sfogar io vo', sfogar io vo'! Solo mi-
Now he shall pay, At last shall pay. O for the
O.
sfogar io vo', sfogar io vo'!
Now he shall pay, At last shall pay.
M.
sfogar io vo', sfogar io vo'!
Now he shall pay, At last shall pay.
tr
tr
mfp
fp
mfp
A.
randolo. stretto in catene, alle mie pene
sight of him Locked in a dungeon! That would my sorrow
mfp
mfp
A.
L.
Leporello (appears, pale and trembling.)
calma darò. Più non sperate di ritrovarlo, più non cercate
Somewhat allay. Seek him no longer, You will not find him, It is too late now,

Donna Anna, Elvira and Zerlina.
A.
E.
Z.
Cos' è? fa-vel-la! cos' è? fa-
We come for vengeance. Where is he
Don Octavio.
O.
Cos' è? fa-vel-la! cos' è? fa-
We come for vengeance. Where is he
Masetto.
M.
Cos' è? fa-vel-la! cos' è? fa-
We come for vengeance. Where is he
L.
Lon-tano an-dò, lon-tano an-dò. Ven-ne un co-los-so,
He's far a-way, Yes, far a-way. There came a gi-ant . . .
f
p
f
vel-la! Via pre-sto, sbriga-ti! via presto, sbriga-ti!
hid-den? Come, tell us, out with it! Where is he, out with it!
vel-la! Via pre-sto, sbriga-ti! via presto, sbriga-ti!
hid-den? Come, tell us, out with it! Where is he, out with it!
vel-la! Via pre-sto, sbriga-ti! via presto, sbriga-ti!
hid-den? Come, tell us, out with it! Where is he, out with it!
venne un co-losso— Ma se non pos-so, ma se non
All made of mar-ble, Yes, made of mar-ble. See how I
p
f
p
f
p

A.
E.
Z.
O.
M.
L.
Pre-sto fa-
Tell us Where
Pre-sto fa-
Tell us Where
Pre-sto fa-
Tell us Where
pos-so, ma se non pos-so, ma se non pos-so, ma se non pos-so—
shud-der. See how I shud-der. See how I shud-der. See how I shud-der.
vel-la, sbri-ga-ti!
is he, Out with it!
vel-la, sbri-ga-ti!
is he, Out with it!
vel-la, sbri-ga-ti!
is he, Out with it!
Leporello.
Tra fumo e fuo-co— ba-da-te un po-co—
As I was say-ing· Came through that door way,
l'uo-mo di sas-so— fer-ma-te il pas-so— giu-sto là sot-to—
Seized on my mas-ter, Seized him and held him. Fire and smoke came

L.
die-de il gran bot - to — giu - sto là il dia - vo - lo se'l tran - gu -
Out of the ground and . . . Down went my mas - ter and van - ished be -
cresc.
f
A.
E.
Z.
Stel - - le! che sen - to!
Ah! That ex - plains it!
O.
Stel - - le! che sen - to!
Ah! That ex - plains it!
M.
Stel - - le! che sen - to!
Ah! That ex - plains it!
L.
giò! Ve - ro è l'e - ven - to.
low. That is what hap - pened.
p
f
p
cresc.
f
Donna Anna.
A.
Ah, cer - to è l'om - bra che l'incon -
Ah! 'twas the ghost who sent him be -
Donna Elvira.
E.
Ah, cer - to è l'om - - bra che m'in - con -
I saw the ghost who sent him be -
Zerlina.
Z.
Ah, cer - to è
I saw it
Don Octavio.
O.
Ah, cer - to è
I saw it
p

A.
trò, Ah! cer - to è l'om - - bra
low. Ah! 'twas the ghost who
E.
trò, Ah! cer - to è l'om - - bra
low Ah, 'twas the ghost who
Z.
l'ombra, Ah! cer - to è l'om - - bra
al - so. Ah! 'twas the ghost who
O.
l'ombra, Ah! cer - to è l'om - - bra
al - so. Ah! 'twas the ghost who
Masetto.
M.
Ah! cer - to è l'om - - bra, è l'om - - bra
Ah, 'twas the ghost, 'twas the ghost who
A.
che l'in - con - trò, ah! cer-to è l'om-bra,
sent him be - low. I saw it, I saw it,
E.
che m'in - con - trò, ah! cer-to è l'om-bra,
sent him be - low. I saw it, I saw it,
Z.
che m'in - con - trò, ah! cer-to è l'om-bra,
sent him be - low. I saw it, I saw it,
O.
che m'in - con - trò, ah! cer-to è l'om-bra,
sent him be - low. I saw it, I saw it,
M.
che m'in - con - trò, ah! cer-to è l'om-bra,
sent him be - low. I saw it, I saw it,

A. ah! cer - to, cer - to e l'om - - - - bra che
I saw, I saw the ghost who sent

F. ah! cer-to, ah cer - to e l'om-bra che
I saw it. I saw the ghost who sent

Z. ah! cer - to, cer - to e l'om - - bra che m'in - -
I saw, I saw the ghost who sent him

O. ah! cer-to e l'om - bra che m'in - -
I saw it! I saw it! It sent

M. ah! cer - - - to e l'om - - bra che m'in - -
I saw the ghost who sent him

A. l'in - con - trò.
him be - low.

F. m'in - con - trò.
him be - low.

Z. con - trò.
be - low.

O. con - trò.
him be - low.

M. con trò.
be - low.

cresc. ***f***

Larghetto.
289
Don Octavio.
(to Donna Anna.)
Or che tut-ti, o mio te-so-ro! ven-di-ca-ti siam dal
Now that Heav-en has tak-en venge-ance, Turn to glad-ness, leave your
Str.
p
cie-lo, por-gi, por-gi, a me un ri-sto-ro, non mi
sor-row, O re-mem-ber the one who loves you, Dear-est
Wind sustain
Fag.
far lan-guire an-cor.
heart, be not un-kind.
Donna Anna.
Lascia, o ca-ro! un an-no an-
Let me, dear-est, for one year
Vlns.
co-ra, al-lo sfo-go del mio cor.
long-er Keep my fath-er's death in mind,
cresc.
Al de-sio di chi t'a-do-ra,
Then, but then, I'll prove, I swear it,
D. Octavio.
Al de-sio di chi m'a-do-ra, ce-der deve un fi-do a-
Then, but then, you'll prove, O swear it, Ev-er faith-ful, ev-er
p

 (giving Don O. her hand.)

A.
fi - do un fi - do a - mor.
ev - er ev - er kind.
(to Donna A. and Don O.)
Donna Elvira.
E.
Io men vado in un ri - ti - ro, a fi - nir la vi - ta
I will hide me in a clois - ter, There to fast and pray and
O.
fi - do un fi - do a - mor.
ev - er ev - er kind.
mi - a!
pon - der.
Zerlina.
Z.
Noi, Ma - setto, a casa an - diamo! a cenar in compa - gni - a.
Happy, hand in hand, Ma - set - to, Home togeth - er let us wan - der.
Masetto.
M.
Noi, Zer - lina, a casa an - diamo! a cenar in compa - gni - a.
Hap py, hand in hand, Zer - li - na, Home togeth - er let us wan - der.
Leporello.
L.
Ed io vado all' o - ste -
May I pres - ent - ly in -
Zerlina.
Re - sti dunque quel birbon, con Pro - ser - pina e Plu -
Leave the ras - cal ly - ing, then, Safe - ly shut in Plu - to's
Masetto.
Re - sti dunque quel birbon, con Pro - ser - pina e Plu -
Leave the ras - cal ly - ing, then, Safe - ly shut in Plu - to's
ri - a a tro - var padron miglior. Re - sti dunque quel birbon, con Pro - ser - pina e Plu -
yon - der Inn a bet - ter mas - ter find. Leave the ras - cal ly - ing, then, Safe - ly shut in Plu - to's
f

Z.
ton, con Pro-ser - pi - na e Plu-ton. E noi
den, Safe-ly shut in Plu - to's den. And, to
M.
ton, con Pro-ser - pi - na e Plu-ton. E noi
den, Safe-ly shut in Plu - to's den. And, to
L.
ton, con Pro-ser - pi - na e Plu-ton. E noi
den, Safe-ly shut in Plu - to's den. And, to
Fl.
Vln.
p
tr
Z.
tut - ti, o buo - na - gen-te, ri-pe - tiam al - le - gra - mente l'an-ti -
ban - ish mel - an - cho-ly, Sing, good peo - ple, all be jol - ly, Sing the
M.
tut - ti, o buo - na gen-te, ri-pe - tiam al - le - gra-men-te l'an-ti -
ban - ish mel - an - cho-ly, Sing, good peo - ple, all be jol - ly, Sing the
L.
tut - ti, o buo - na gen-te, ri-pe - tiam al - le - gra-men-te l'an-ti -
ban - ish mel - an - cho-ly, Sing, good peo - ple, all be jol - ly, Sing the
tr
tr
Z.
chis-si-ma can-zon, l'an-ti-chis-si-ma can-zon, l'an-ti-chis-si-ma can-zon:
old, old song a-gain, Sing the old, old song a-gain, Sing the old, old song a-gain.
M.
chis-si-ma can-zon, l'an-ti-chis-si-ma can-zon, l'an-ti-chis-si-ma can-zon:
old, old song a-gain, Sing the old, old song a-gain, Sing the old, old song a-gain.
L.
chis-si-ma can-zon, l'an-ti-chis-si-ma can-zon, l'an-ti-chis-si-ma can-zon:
old, old song a-gain, Sing the old, old song a-gain, Sing the old, old song a-gain.

Presto.

Donna Anna. *sotto voce*

A. Que - sto è il fin di chi fa mal, di chi fa mal, Que - sto è il fin,

So do all de - ceiv - ers end, de - ceiv - ers end, So they end,

Str. *p*

Donna Elvira. *f*

E. Que - sto è il fin,

So they end,

Zerlina. *sotto voce*

Z. Que - sto è il

So do

Don Octavio. *f*

O. Que - sto è il fin,

So they end,

Masetto. *f*

M. Que - sto è il fin,

So they end,

Leporello. *f*

L. Que - sto è il fin,

So they end,

f *Wind.* *f* *p*

Zerlina.

Z. fin di chi fa mal, di chi fa mal.

all de - ceiv - ers end, de - ceiv - ers end,

f

Donna Anna and Donna Elvira.
(unis.)
A.
E.
Que - sto è il fin, que - sto è il fin di chi fa mal, di
So they end, So do all de - ceiv - ers end, de -
Z.
Que-sto è il fin, que - sto è il fin di chi fa mal, di
So they end, So do all de - ceiv - ers end, de -
O.
Que-sto è il fin, que - sto è il fin di chi fa mal, di
So they end, So do all de-ceiv - ers end, de -
M.
Que - sto è il fin di chi fa mal, di
So do all de-ceiv - ers end, de -
L.
Que - sto è il fin di chi fa mal, di
So do all de-ceiv - ers end, de -
tr
A.
E.
chi fa mal, di chi fa mal, que-sto è il fin di
ceiv - ers end, they all shall end. So do all wrong-
Z.
chi fa mal, di chi fa mal, que-sto è il fin di
ceiv - ers end, they all shall end. So do all wrong-
O.
chi fa mal, di chi fa mal, que-sto è il fin di
ceiv - ers end, they all shall end. So do all wrong-
M.
chi fa mal, di chi fa mal, que-sto è il fin di
ceiv - ers end, they all shall end. So do all wrong-
L.
chi fa mal, di chi fa mal, que-sto è il fin di
ceiv - ers end, they all shall end. So do all wrong-
tr
tr

A.
E.
chi fa mal, di chi fa mal. E de'
do - ers end, wrong - do - ers end. Rakes, be -
Z.
O.
M.
L.
Vlns.
Tutti
per- - fi - di la mor-
tray - - ers, all take warn -

A.
E.
- - te al la vi - ta è
- - ing While there's time, (while there's
Z.
- - te al la vi - ta è
- - ing While there's time, (while there's
O.
- - te al la vi - ta è
- - ing While there's time, (while there's
M.
- - te al la vi - ta è
- - ing While there's time (while there's
L.
- - te al - la
- - ing (While there's
Wind
Cello
sem - pre, è sem - pre u - gual, è sempre u - gual.
time), still your ways to mend, Your ways to mend.
sem - pre è sem - pre u - gual, è sempre u - gual.
time), still your ways to mend, Your ways to mend.
sem - pre, è sem - pre u - gual, è sempre u - gual.
time), still your ways to mend, Your ways to mend.
sem - pre, è sem - pre u - gual, è sempre u - gual.
time), still your ways to mend, Your ways to mend.
vi - ta è sem - pre u - gual, è sempre u - gual.
time), still your ways to mend, Your ways to mend.

A.
E.
E de' per- -fi - di la
Rakes, be - tray - - ers, all take
Z.
E' de' per- -fi - di la
Rakes, be - tray - - ers, all take
O.
E de' per- -fi - di la
Rakes, be - tray - - ers, all take
M.
E de' per- -fi - di la
Rakes, be - tray - - ers, all take
L.
E de' per- -fi - di la
Rakes, be - tray - - ers, all take
mor - - - - te al -
warn- - - - ing While
mor - - - - te
warn- - - - ing

A.
F.
la vi ta è sem - pre è sem -
there's time, (while there's time), still your ways,
Z.
la vi ta è sem - pre u - gual,
there's time, (while there's time), to mend
O.
la vi ta è sem - pre, è sem -
there's time, (while there's time), still your ways,
M.
la vi ta è sem - pre, è sem -
there's time, (while there's time), still your ways
L.
p
al - la vi - ta è sem -
While there's time still your ways,
p
pre, è sem -
your ways
è sem -
your ways
pre,
to mend,
è sem -
your ways

A.
E.
- pre u-gual, al - la vi - ta è sem - pre u - gual,
to mend, While there's time Your ways to mend,
Z.
- pre u - gual, al - la vi - ta è sem - pre u - gual,
to mend, While there's time Your ways to mend,
O.
pre u - gual, al - la vi - ta è sem - pre u - gual,
to mend, While there's time Your ways to mend,
M.
pre u - gual, al - la vi - ta è sem - pre u - gual,
to mend, While there's time Your ways to mend,
L.
pre u - gual, al - la vi - ta è sem - pre u - gual,
to mend, While there's time Your ways to mend,
f
A.
E.
al - la vi - ta è sem - pre u - gual, è sem - pre u -
while there's time your ways to mend. So mend your
Z.
al - la vi - ta è sem - pre u - gual, è sem - pre u -
while there's time your ways to mend. So mend your
O.
al - la vi - ta è sem - pre u - gual, è sem - pre u -
while there's time your ways to mend. So mend your
M.
al - la vi - ta è sem - pre u - gual, è sem - pre u -
while there's time your ways to mend. So mend your
L.
al - la vi - ta è sem - pre u - gual, è sem - pre u -
while there's time your ways to mend. So mend your

End of the Opera.